WE PATTER ALONG IN THE DUST AGAIN

See "Old Aunt Mary's."

CHILD CLASSICS
THE FOURTH READER

By

GEORGIA ALEXANDER
and
GRACE ALEXANDER

WITH PICTURES BY

WALTER CRANE, HOWARD CHANDLER CHRISTY, FRIEDRICH AUGUST
KAULBACH, JOHN CECIL CLAY, REGINALD BIRCH, HUGH THOMSON,
ARTHUR RACKHAM, E. M. ASHE AND LUCY FITCH PERKINS

INDIANAPOLIS
THE BOBBS-MERRILL COMPANY
PUBLISHERS

Set up, Plated and Printed March, 1909
Reprinted September, 1909

PRINTERS AND BINDERS

PREFACE

When a community takes upon itself the responsibility of teaching its children to read it should assume at the same time that greater responsibility of teaching them what to read. A series of school readers designed to teach the art of reading should therefore carry in its pages that which will train in the choice of reading.

The cultivation of this habit should begin with the primer. From the first page the child should go to the book to get thought, not merely exercise in word calling. The succeeding books should gradually develop a high and catholic taste, and foster this taste by establishing early the custom of reading standard books at home.

Child Classics have been prepared with these principles in view. In addition to providing a definite and flexible method for teaching beginners to read, effort has been made to include only material that may justly be called classic. The selections chosen have borne the repeated test of school-room trial both as to interest and careful grading. Care has also been taken to present a variety of appeal through the heroic, the imaginative, the humorous, the ethical and the realistic.

Recognizing that in school readers abridgments are necessary if the child is to be acquainted with a wide range of literature, the original text has been cut whenever the whole was of a length impossible to reproduce within the given space, or when this whole was in the judgment of the editors unsuited to the child's needs at this time.

Special attention has been given to the biographies of authors in the desire to make them interesting as well as instructive. As great men truly furnish the "very marrow of the world's history," a vivid personal impression, especially glimpses of their childhood when ideals were forming, outvalues many dates and other encyclopedic details.

Lists of books for home reading edited for this series by Hamilton Wright Mabie are included in the *Third, Fourth* and *Fifth Readers,* not

V

only for the direction for the child and the guidance of the teacher, but also to obtain the coöperation of parents in fixing in habit the taste for good literature created by the text books themselves.

The notes appended for study have been prepared, not only to explain the text, but to further the child's interest in the author and the selection. At the end of each book will be found suggestions to teachers. These have been made unusually concrete and full in the desire to throw increased light on the teaching of this, the most important subject in the school curriculum. It is hoped that a measure of success has attended the undertaking, and that teachers and pupils to whom the books may come will take new joy in their work.

It is a pleasure to thank Miss Nebraska Cropsey, Assistant Superintendent of Schools in Indianapolis, for suggestions concerning the teaching of reading covering a period of twenty years; Miss Adelaide Baylor, Superintendent of Schools at Wabash, who has carefully read the text and made valuable criticisms, and the many teachers who have tested the books in their classes.

G. A.

Acknowledgment is made for permission to use selections from the writings of Andrew Lang, to Longmans, Green and Company; from Louisa M. Alcott, to Little, Brown and Company; from Joaquin Miller, to the Whitaker and Ray Company; from David Starr Jordan, to A. C. McClurg and Company; from Frank R. Stockton, to Charles Scribner's Sons; for selections from Bryant's *Complete Poetical Works*, to D. Appleton and Company; and for *The Merry Pranks of Till Owl-glass*, to the Lothrop, Lee and Shepard Company. Acknowledgment is also made for permission to use an illustration from *Puck of Pook's Hill*, to Doubleday, Page and Company; and from Dickens's *Christmas Carol*, to G. P. Putnam's Sons.

The selections from the writings of Henry Wadsworth Longfellow, J. T. Trowbridge, John Greenleaf Whittier, Alice Cary, and Josephine Preston Peabody are used by special arrangement with Houghton, Mifflin and Company.

CONTENTS

CONTENTS

CONTENTS

Hark, where my blossomed pear-tree in the hedge
Leans to the field and scatters on the clover
Blossoms and dewdrops—at the bent spray's edge—
That's the wise thrush; he sings each song twice over,
Lest you should think he never could recapture
The first fine careless rapture!
    "Home-Thoughts from Abroad."   Robert Browning.

THE FOURTH READER

TOM, THE CHIMNEY SWEEP

By Charles Kingsley

I

Once upon a time there was a little chimney-sweep, and his name was Tom. He lived in a great town in the north country, where there were plenty of chimneys to sweep, and plenty of money for Tom to earn and his master to spend.

He could not read nor write; and he never washed himself, for there was no water up the court where he lived. He had never been taught to say his prayers. He cried half his time, and laughed the other half. He cried when he had to climb the dark flues. And he laughed when he was tossing halfpennies with the other boys, or playing leap-frog over the posts.

As for chimney-sweeping, and being hungry, and being beaten, he took all that for the way of the world, like the rain and snow and thunder, and stood manfully with his back to it till it was over. Then he shook his ears and was as jolly as ever; and thought of the fine times coming, when he would be a man, and a master-sweep, and wear velveteens and ankle-jacks, and keep a white bulldog with one gray ear, and carry her puppies in his pocket, just like a man. And he would have apprentices, one, two, three, if he could.

One day a smart little groom rode into the court where Tom lived. Tom was just behind a wall, but the groom saw him, and halloed to him to know where Mr. Grimes, the chimney-sweep, lived. Now, Mr. Grimes was Tom's own master, and Tom was a good man of business and always civil to customers.

Mr. Grimes was to come up next morning to Sir John Harthover's at the Place, for his old chimney-sweep was gone and the chimneys wanted sweeping. And so the groom rode away.

Now, I dare say, you never got up at three o clock on a midsummer morning. Some people get up then because they want to catch salmon; and some because they want to climb Alps; and a great many more because they must, like Tom.

But, I assure you, that three o'clock on a midsummer morning is the pleasantest time of all the twenty-four hours, and all the three hundred and sixty-five days; and why every one does not get up then, I never could tell. But Tom was as pert as a game-cock, and ready to get up.

So he and his master set out; Grimes rode the donkey

in front, and Tom and the brushes walked behind; out of the court, and up the street, past the closed window shutters, and the roofs all shining gray in the gray dawn.

Then they were out in the real country, and plodding along the black dusty road, between black slag walls, with no sound but the groaning and thumping of the pit-engine in the next field.

Soon the road grew white, and the walls likewise; and at the walls' foot grew long grass and gay flowers, all drenched with dew; and instead of the groaning of the pit-engine, they heard the skylark high up in the air, and the pit-bird warbling in the sedges, as he had warbled all night long.

All else was silent. For old Mother Earth was still fast asleep; and, like many pretty people, she looked still prettier asleep than awake.

The great elm trees in the gold-green meadows were fast asleep above, and the cows fast asleep beneath them. The few clouds which were about were fast asleep likewise, and so tired that they had lain down on the earth to rest, in long white flakes and bars, among the stems of the elm trees.

On they went; and Tom looked and looked, for he never had been so far into the country before; and longed to get over a gate, and pick buttercups, and look for birds in the hedge; but Mr. Grimes was a man of business, and would not have heard of that.

II

Soon they came up with a poor Irishwoman, trudging along with a bundle at her back. She had a gray shawl over her head, and a crimson madder petticoat; so you may be sure she came from Galway. She had neither shoes nor stockings, and limped along as if she were tired and footsore. But she was a very tall, handsome woman, with bright gray eyes, and heavy black hair hanging about her cheeks.

She walked beside Tom, and talked to him, and asked him where he lived, and what he knew, and all about himself, till Tom thought he had never met such a pleasant-spoken woman. And she asked him, at last, whether he said his prayers, and seemed sad when he told her that he knew no prayers to say.

At last, at the bottom of a hill, they came to a spring; not such a spring as you see here, which soaks up out of a white gravel in the bog, among red fly-catchers, and pink bottle-heath, but a real north country limestone fountain.

"I wish I might go and dip my head in," said poor little Tom. "It must be as good as putting it under the town pump; and there is no beadle here to drive a chap away."

"Thou come along," said Grimes, "what dost want with washing thyself?"

"I don't care for you," said Tom, and ran down to the stream, and began washing his face.

Grimes was very sulky, so he dashed at him and began beating him. But Tom was accustomed to that, and got his head safe between Grimes's legs, and kicked his shins with all his might.

"Are you not ashamed of yourself, Thomas Grimes?" cried the Irishwoman over the wall.

Grimes looked up, startled at her knowing his name; but all he answered was, "No, nor never was yet;" and went on beating Tom.

"True for you. If you ever had been ashamed of yourself, you would have gone over into Vendale long ago."

"What do you know about Vendale?" shouted Grimes; but he left off beating Tom.

"I know about Vendale, and about you, too."

"You do?" shouted Grimes; and leaving Tom, he climbed up over the wall and faced the woman. Tom thought he was going to strike her; but she looked him too full and fierce in the face for that.

Grimes seemed quite cowed, and got on his donkey without another word.

"Stop!" said the Irishwoman. "I have one more word for you both; for you will both see me again before all is over. Those that wish to be clean, clean they will be; and those that wish to be foul, foul they will be. Remember." And she turned away, and through a gate into a meadow. Grimes stood still a moment, like a man who had been stunned. Then he rushed after her shouting,

"You come back." But when he got into the meadow, the woman was not there.

And now they had gone three miles or more, and came to Sir John's lodge-gates.

III

They walked up a great lime avenue, a full mile long. Between the stems of the trees Tom peeped trembling at the horns of the sleeping deer, which stood up among the ferns. Tom had never seen such enormous trees, and as he looked up, he fancied that the blue sky rested on their heads.

Tom and his master went round the back way, and a very long way round it was, and into a little back door, where the ash-boy let them in. In a passage the house-keeper met them, in such a flowered chintz dressing-gown, that Tom mistook her for my lady herself. She gave Grimes solemn orders about "You will take care of this, and take care of that," as if he was going up the chimneys, and not Tom. Grimes listened, and said every now and then, under his voice, "You'll mind that, you little beggar?" and Tom did mind, all at least that he could.

The housekeeper turned them into a grand room, all covered up in sheets of brown paper, and bade them begin, in a lofty and tremendous voice. So after a whimper or two and a kick from his master, into the grate Tom went, and up the chimney, while a housemaid stayed in the room to watch the furniture.

How many chimneys Tom swept I can not say; but he swept so many that he got quite tired, and puzzled, too, and he fairly lost his way in them. Not that he cared much for that, though he was in pitchy darkness. He was as much at home in a chimney as a mole is underground. But at last, coming down as he thought the right chimney, he came down the wrong one, and found himself standing on the hearthrug in a room the like of which he had never seen before.

Tom had never seen the like. He had never been in gentlefolk's rooms but when the carpets were all up, and the curtains down, and the furniture huddled together under a cloth, and the pictures covered with aprons and dusters. He had often enough wondered what the rooms were like when they were all ready for the quality to sit in. And now he saw, and he thought the sight very pretty.

The room was all dressed in white—white window-curtains, white bed-curtains, white furniture, and white walls, with just a few lines of pink here and there. The carpet was all over gay little flowers; and the walls were hung with pictures in gilt frames, which amused Tom very much. There were pictures of ladies and gentlemen, and pictures of horses and dogs.

The next thing he saw, and that too puzzled him, was

2—4th

a washing-stand, with ewers and basins, and soap and brushes, and towels, and a large bath full of clean water —what a heap of things all for washing! "She must be a very dirty lady," thought Tom, "to want as much scrubbing as all that."

IV

And then, looking toward the bed, he saw that dirty lady, and held his breath with astonishment.

Under the snow-white coverlet, upon the snow-white pillow, lay the most beautiful little girl that Tom had ever seen. Her cheeks were almost as white as the pillow, and her hair was like threads of gold spread all about over the bed. She might have been as old as Tom, or maybe a year or two older; but Tom did not think of that.

He thought only of her delicate skin and golden hair, and wondered whether she was a real live person, or one of the wax dolls he had seen in the shops. But when he saw her breathe, he made up his mind that she was alive, and stood staring at her, as if she had been an angel out of Heaven.

No. She can not be dirty. She never could have been dirty, thought Tom to himself. And then he thought, "Are all people like that when they are washed?" And he looked at his own wrist, and tried to rub the soot off, and wondered whether it ever would come off. "Cer-

tainly I should look much prettier then, if I grew at all
like her."

And looking round, he suddenly saw, standing close to
him, a little ugly, black, ragged figure, with bleared eyes
and grinning white teeth. He turned on it angrily.
What did such a little black ape want in that sweet
young lady's room? And behold, it was himself, reflected
in a great mirror, the like of which Tom had never seen
before.

And Tom, for the first time in his life, found out that
he was dirty, and burst into tears with shame and anger;
and turned to sneak up the chimney again and hide. He
upset the fender and threw the fire-irons down, with a noise
as of ten thousand tin kettles tied to ten thousand dogs'
tails.

Up jumped the little white lady in her bed, and seeing
Tom, screamed as shrill as any peacock. In rushed a
stout old nurse from the next room, and seeing Tom likewise, made up her mind that he had come to rob, plunder,
destroy, and burn. She dashed at him as he lay over the
fender, so fast that she caught him by the jacket.

But she did not hold him. Tom doubled under the
good lady's arm, across the room, and out of the window
in a moment.

He did not need to drop out, though he would have
done so, bravely enough, or even to let himself down a
spout, which would have been an old game to him.

But all under the window spread a tree, with great leaves and sweet white flowers, almost as big as his head. It was a magnolia, I suppose; but Tom knew nothing about that, and cared less; for down the tree he went, like a cat, and across the garden lawn, and over the iron railings, and up the park toward the wood.

From "The Water Babies." Abridged.

THE SEA

By Barry Cornwall (Bryan Waller Procter)

The sea! the sea! the open sea!
The blue, the fresh, the ever free!
Without a mark, without a bound,
It runneth the earth's wide regions round;
It plays with the clouds; it mocks the skies;
Or like a cradled creature lies.

I'm on the sea! I'm on the sea!
I am where I would ever be;
With the blue above, and the blue below,
And silence wheresoe'er I go;
If a storm should come and awake the deep,
What matter?   I shall ride and sleep.

I love, oh, how I love to ride
On the fierce, foaming, bursting tide,

When every mad wave drowns the moon,
Or whistles aloft his tempest tune,
And tells how goeth the world below,
And why the sou'west blasts do blow.

I never was on the dull, tame shore,
But I loved the great sea more and more,
And backward flew to her billowy breast,
Like a bird that seeketh its mother's nest;
And a mother she was, and is, to me;
For I was born on the open sea!

The waves were white, and red the morn,
In the noisy hour when I was born;
And the whale it whistled, the porpoise rolled,
And the dolphins bared their backs of gold;

And never was heard such an outcry wild
As welcomed to life the ocean-child!

I've lived since then, in calm and strife,
Full fifty summers, a sailor's life,
With wealth to spend, and power to range,
But never have sought nor sighed for change;
And Death, whenever he comes to me,
Shall come on the wild, unbounded sea!

THE DISCONTENTED PENDULUM

RETOLD FROM JANE TAYLOR

It is twenty minutes past eleven o'clock on a summer morning in the hallway of a colonial mansion. In the corner stands an old grandfather's clock with its long pendulum swinging solemnly backward and forward as it has done for fifty years. Suddenly a slight shiver passes over its entire frame. The clock has stopped!

The Dial. (*Blue in the face.*) What is the matter?

The Hands. (*Looking round.* That's what we should like to know!

The Wheels. (*With a whir.*) And we!

The Weights. (*With great gravity.*) And we!

The Pendulum. (*With a faint tick.*) I confess myself to be the sole cause. I am willing to give my reason. I am simply tired of ticking.

The Dial. (*Holding up its hands.*) You lazy wire!

The Pendulum. Very good! It is easy enough for you, Mistress Dial, who have always, as everybody knows, set yourself up above me—it is vastly easy for you, I say, to accuse other people of laziness. You have had nothing to do all your life but to stare people in the face and to amuse yourself with watching all that goes on in the kitchen. How would you like to be shut up for life in this dark closet and wag backward and forward year after year as I do?

The Dial. Is there not a window in your house on purpose for you to look through?

The Pendulum. For all that it is very dark here and although there is a window, I dare not stop even for an instant to look out. I tell you again, I am tired of ticking! How many times do you suppose I should have to tick in the course of only the next twenty-four hours?

The Minute Hand. (*Counting quickly on its fingers and in a low voice.*) Sixty, times sixty, times twenty-four; (*Aloud.*) Eighty-six thousand four hundred times.

The Pendulum. Exactly so. The very thought of it is enough to tire one. When I begin to multiply the strokes of one day by those of months and years, is it any wonder that I have decided to stop?

The Dial. (*Who has been laughing behind the hands, now looks gravely forth.*) Dear Pendulum, I am really astonished that such a useful, industrious person as yourself should have been seized by this sudden weariness. You have done a great deal of work in your time, as have we all, and are likely to do; which, although it may fatigue us to think of, the question is, whether it will fatigue us to do. Now do me tne favor to give about half a dozen strokes.

The Pendulum.   With pleasure! (*Ticks six times.*)

The Dial.   Now, did that tire you? Of course not!

The Pendulum.   It is not of six strokes that I complain, nor of sixty, but of millions!

The Dial.   Very good.   But recollect that though you may think of a million strokes in an instant, you are required to make but one, and that, however often you may hereafter have to swing, a moment will always be given to you to swing in.

The Pendulum.   I suppose that is true.   I had not looked at it in that way.   I am quite convinced.

The Dial.   Then I hope we shall all immediately return to our duty.   It is time for the squire to be back from his walk.

(*The wheels begin to turn, the hands to move and the pendulum to swing.*)

The Dial.   (*A sunbeam striking its happy face.*) Here he comes!

(*Squire Brown enters, puts his hat on the chair.   He suddenly looks at the clock, then pulls out his watch.*)

Squire Brown.   Bless me!   My watch has gained half an hour!

BLESS ME! MY WATCH HAS GAINED

THE INCHCAPE ROCK

By Robert Southey

No stir in the air, no stir in the sea,
The ship was still as she could be;
Her sails from Heaven received no motion;
Her keel was steady in the ocean.

Without either sign or sound of their shock,
The waves flowed over the Inchcape Rock;
So little they rose, so little they fell,
They did not move the Inchcape Bell.

The Abbot of Aberbrothok
Had placed that bell on the Inchcape Rock;
On a buoy in the storm it floated and swung,
And over the waves its warning rung.

When the rock was hid by the surge's swell,
The mariners heard the warning bell;
And then they knew the perilous rock
And blessed the Abbot of Aberbrothok.

The sun in heaven was shining gay;
All things were joyful on that day;
The sea-birds screamed as they wheeled round,
And there was joyance in their sound.

The buoy of the Inchcape Bell was seen
A darker speck on the ocean green;
Sir Ralph the Rover walked his deck,
And he fixed his eye on the darker speck.

He felt the cheering power of spring,
It made him whistle, it made him sing;
His heart was mirthful to excess,
But the Rover's mirth was wickedness.

His eye was on the Inchcape float;
Quoth he, " My men, put out the boat,
And row me to the Inchcape Rock,
And I'll plague the priest of Aberbrothok."

The boat is lowered, the boatmen row,
And to the Inchcape Rock they go;
Sir Ralph bent over from the boat,
And he cut the bell from the Inchcape float.

Down sank the bell, with a gurgling sound,
The bubbles rose and burst around;
Quoth Sir Ralph, " The next who comes to the Rock
Won't bless the Abbot of Aberbrothok!"

Sir Ralph the Rover sailed away,
He scoured the seas for many a day;
And now grown rich with plundered store,
He steers his course for Scotland's shore.

So thick a haze o'erspreads the sky,
They can not see the sun on high:
The wind hath blown a gale all day;
At evening it hath died away.

On the deck the Rover takes his stand;
So dark it is they see no land.
Quoth Sir Ralph, "It will be brighter soon,
For there is the dawn of the rising moon."

"Canst hear," said one, "the breakers roar?
For methinks we should be near the shore."
"Now where we are I can not tell,
But I wish I could hear the Inchcape Bell."

They hear no sound; the swell is strong;
Though the wind hath fallen, they drift along
Till the vessel strikes with a shivering shock:
"O Christ! it is the Inchcape Rock!"

Sir Ralph the Rover tore his hair;
He cursed himself in his despair:
The waves rush in on every side;
The ship is sinking beneath the tide.

But, even in his dying fear,
One dreadful sound could the Rover hear,—
A sound as if with the Inchcape Bell
The devil below was ringing his knell.

TURNING THE GRINDSTONE

By Benjamin Franklin

When I was a little boy, I remember that one cold morning in winter I was accosted by a smiling man with an ax on his shoulder.

"My pretty boy," said he, "has your father a grindstone?"

"Yes, sir," said I.

"You are a fine little fellow," said he; "will you let me grind my ax on it?"

His words of flattery made me happy, and I was glad to do anything he wanted. I told him that the grindstone was in the shop. Patting me on the head, he said, "My man, will you get me a little hot water?" How could I refuse? I ran and soon brought it. "How old are you, and what is your name?" he next asked me. Without waiting for me to tell him, he then said, "You are a fine little man, the finest boy that I have ever seen. Will you just turn the grindstone a few minutes for me?"

All these kind words made me so very happy that I went to work with a will, and bitterly did I rue the day. It was a new ax, and I toiled and tugged till I was almost tired out. The school bell rang, and I could not get away. Soon my hands were blistered, and the ax was half ground. However, by and by it was sharpened. Then the man told me roughly to be off to school.

"You are a truant," he said, "the teacher will be after you." These words made me sad. It was hard to turn the grindstone, but to be called a truant was too much.

His words sank deep into my mind. I have thought of them many times. I now never hear a man flattering any one, but that I think of turning the grindstone. I know that man has an ax to grind. Look out for flattery. There are many men who will want you to turn the grindstone.

Adapted.

THE CORN-SONG

By John Greenleaf Whittier

Heap high the farmer's wintry hoard!
  Heap high the golden corn!
No richer gift has Autumn poured
  From out her lavish horn!

Through vales of grass and meads of flowers
  Our plows their furrows made,
While on the hills the sun and showers
  Of changeful April played

We dropped the seed o'er hill and plain
  Beneath the sun of May,
And frightened from our sprouting grain
  The robber crows away.

All through the long, bright days of June
　　Its leaves grew green and fair,
And waved in hot midsummer's noon
　　Its soft and yellow hair.

And now, with autumn's moonlit eves,
　　Its harvest-time has come,
We pluck away the frosted leaves,
　　And bear the treasure home.

Then shame on all the proud and vain,
　　Whose folly laughs to scorn
The blessing of our hardy grain,
　　Our wealth of golden corn!

　　　　　　　　　　　　　　　　Abridged.

A LETTER TO HIS SON

By Robert Southey

Leyden, July 2, 1825.

My Dear Cuthbert, — I have a present for you from Lodowijk William Bilderdijk, a very nice good boy who is the age of your sister Isabel. It is a book of Dutch verses which you and I will read together when I come home.

When he was a little boy and was learning to write, his father, who is very much such a father as I am, made little verses for him to write in his copy-book; so many that leave was asked to print them. . . . Lodowijk will write his name and yours in the book. He is a very gentle good boy and I hope that one of these days somewhere or other he and you may meet.

I must tell you about his stork. You should know that there are a great many storks in this country and that it is thought a very wicked thing to hurt them. They make their nests, which are as large as a great clothes-basket, upon the houses and churches, and frequently, when a house or church is built, a wooden frame is made on the top for the storks to build in.

Out of one of these nests a young stork had fallen and somebody wishing to keep him in a garden cut one of his wings. The stork tried to fly, but fell in Mr. Bilderdijk's

garden and was found there one morning almost dead.
His legs and his bill had lost their color and were grown
pale.   He would have died if Mrs. Bilderdijk, who is kind
to everybody and everything, had not taken care of him.
She gave him food and he recovered.

The first night they put him in a sort of summer-house
in the garden, which I can not describe to you for I have
not been there myself.   The second night he walked to
the door himself that it might be opened to him.   He was
very fond of Lodowijk and Lodowijk was as fond of his
oyevaar (which is the name for stork in Dutch, though
I am not sure that I have spelled it right).   They used to

3—4th

play together in such a manner that his father says it was a pleasure to see them; for a stork is a large bird, tall and upright, almost as tall as you are or quite.

The *oyevaar* was a bad gardener. He ate snails, but with his great broad foot he did a great deal of mischief, and destroyed all the strawberries and many of the vegetables. But Mr. and Mrs. Bilderdijk did not mind this because the *oyevaar* loved Lodowijk and therefore they loved the *oyevaar*. Sometimes they used to send a mile out of town to buy eels for him when none could be had in Leyden.

The very day I came to the house, the stork flew away. His wings were grown and no doubt he thought it time to get a wife and settle in life. Lodowijk saw him rise in the air and fly away. Lodowijk was very sorry. Not only because he loved the *oyevaar*, but because he was afraid the *oyevaar* would not be able to get his own living and therefore would be starved.

On the second evening, however, the stork came again and pitched upon a wall near. It was in the twilight and storks can not see at all when it is dusk; but whenever Lodowijk called "Oye! Oye!" (which was the way he used to call him) the *oyevaar* turned his head toward the sound. He did not come into the garden. Some fish was placed there for him, but in the morning he was gone and had not eaten it. So we suppose that he is married and living very happily with his mate and that now and then he will come and visit the old friends who were so good to him.

.   .   .   I hope you have been a good boy and done everything that you ought to do while I have been away.
.   .   .   My love to your sisters and to everybody else. I hope Kumpelstilzchen has recovered his health and that Miss Cat is well, and I should like to know whether Miss Fitzrumpel has been given away and if there is another kitten. The Dutch cats do not speak exactly the same language as the English ones. I will tell you how they talk when I come home.

God bless you, my dear Cuthbert.

Your dutiful father,

ROBERT SOUTHEY.

ROBERT OF LINCOLN

By WILLIAM CULLEN BRYANT

Merrily swinging on brier and weed,
  Near to the nest of his little dame,
Over the mountain-side or mead,
  Robert of Lincoln is telling his name:
    "Bob-o'-link, bob-o'-link,
      Spink, spank, spink;
Snug and safe is that nest of ours,
Hidden among the summer flowers.
      Chee, chee, chee."

Robert of Lincoln is gaily drest,
    Wearing a bright black wedding-coat;
White are his shoulders and white his crest.
    Hear him call in his merry note:
       "Bob-o'-link, bob-o'-link,
       Spink, spank, spink;
Look, what a nice new coat is mine,
Sure there was never a bird so fine.
       Chee, chee, chee."

Robert of Lincoln's Quaker wife,
    Pretty and quiet, with plain brown wings,
Passing at home a patient life,
    Broods in the grass while her husband sings:
       "Bob-o'-link, bob-o'-link,
       Spink, spank, spink;
Brood, kind creature; you need not fear
Thieves and robbers while I am here.
       Chee, chee, chee."

Modest and shy as a nun is she;
    One weak chirp is her only note.
Braggart and prince of braggarts is he,
    Pouring boasts from his little throat:
       "Bob-o'-link, bob-o'-link,
       Spink, spank, spink;
Never was I afraid of man;
Catch me, cowardly knaves, if you can.
       Chee, chee, chee."

Six white eggs on a bed of hay,
    Flecked with purple, a pretty sight!
There as the mother sits all day,
    Robert is singing with all his might:
      " Bob-o'-link, bob-o'-link,
        Spink, spank, spink;
Nice good wife, that never goes out,
Keeping house while I frolic about.
        Chee, chee, chee."

Soon as the little ones chip the shell,
    Six wide mouths are open for food;
Robert of Lincoln bestirs him well,
    Gathering seeds for the hungry brood.
      "Bob-o'-link, bob-o'-link,
        Spink, spank, spink;
This new life is likely to be
Hard for a gay young fellow like me.
        Chee, chee, chee."

Summer wanes; the children are grown;
    Fun and frolic no more he knows;
Robert of Lincoln's a humdrum crone;
    Off he flies, and we sing as he goes:
      " Bob-o'-link, bob-o'-link,
        Spink, spank, spink;
When you can pipe that merry old strain,
Robert of Lincoln, come back again.
        Chee, chee, chee."

BARON MÜNCHHAUSEN IN RUSSIA

By R. E. Raspe

There was a real Münchhausen, a German soldier who served Russia in her wars against the Turks in the eighteenth century. But the adventures attributed to him by his biographer are so marvelous that his name has come to stand for any absurd and incredible tale.

I set off on a journey to Russia, in the midst of winter, from a just notion that frost and snow must, of course, mend the roads, which every traveler had described as uncommonly bad through the northern parts of Germany, Poland, Courland, and Livonia. I went on horseback, as it is the most convenient manner of traveling, provided, however, that the rider and horse are in good condition. I was but lightly clothed, and of this I felt the inconvenience the more I advanced northeast. What must not a poor old man have suffered, whom I saw on a bleak common in Poland, lying on the road, helpless, shivering, and hardly having wherewithal to cover his nakedness! I pitied the poor soul. Though I felt the severity of the air myself, I threw my mantle over him, and immediately I heard a voice from the heavens, blessing me for that act of charity, saying,

"You will be rewarded, my son, for this, in time."

I went on; night and darkness overtook me. No sight

or sound of a village was to be met with. The country was covered with snow, and I was unacquainted with the road.

Tired, I alighted, and fastened my horse to something like the pointed stump of a tree, which appeared above the snow. For the sake of safety, I placed my pistols under my arm, and lay down on the snow, where I slept so soundly that I did not open my eyes till full daylight.

Imagine my astonishment, to find myself in the midst of a village, lying in a churchyard; nor was my horse to be seen, but I heard him soon after, neigh somewhere above me. On looking upwards, I beheld him hanging by his bridle to the weather-cock of the steeple. Matters were now very plain to me; the village had been covered with snow overnight; a sudden change of weather had taken place; I had sunk down to the churchyard whilst asleep, gently, and in the same proportion as the snow had melted away. What in the darkness I had taken to be the stump of a little tree appearing above the snow, to which I had tied my horse, proved to have been the cross or weather-cock of the steeple!

Without long consideration, I took one of my pistols, shot the bridle in two, brought down the horse, and proceeded on my journey. (Here the Baron seems to have forgotten his feelings. He should certainly have ordered his horse a feed of corn, after it had fasted so long.)

Abridged.

JERRY, THE MILLER

By John G. Saxe

Beneath the hill you may see the mill
　Of wasting wood and crumbling stone;
The wheel is dripping and clattering still,
　But Jerry, the miller, is dead and gone.

Year after year, early and late,
　Alike in summer and winter weather,
He pecked the stones and calked the gate,
　And mill and miller grew old together.

"Little Jerry!"—'twas all the same,—
　They loved him well who called him so;
And whether he'd ever another name,
　Nobody ever seemed to know.

'Twas, "Little Jerry, come grind my rye";
　And, "Little Jerry, come grind my wheat";
And "Little Jerry" was still the cry,
　From matron bold and maiden sweet.

'Twas "Little Jerry" on every tongue,
　And so the simple truth was told;
For Jerry was little when he was young,
　And Jerry was little when he was old.

But what in size he chanced to lack,
That Jerry made up in being strong;
I've seen a sack upon his back,
As thick as the miller, and quite as long.

Always busy, and always merry,
Always doing his very best,
A notable wag was Little Jerry,
Who uttered well his standing jest.

How Jerry lived is known to fame,
But how he died there's none may know;
One autumn day the rumor came,
"The brook and Jerry are very low."

And then 'twas whispered mournfully,
  The leech had come, and he was dead;
And all the neighbors flocked to see;
  "Poor Little Jerry!" was all they said.

They laid him in his earthly bed,—
  His miller's coat his only shroud;
"Dust to dust," the parson said,
  And all the people wept aloud.

For he had shunned the deadly sin,
  And not a grain of over-toll
Had ever dropped into his bin,
  To weigh upon his parting soul.

Beneath the hill there stands the mill,
  Of wasting wood and crumbling stone;
The wheel is dripping and clattering still,
  But Jerry, the miller, is dead and gone.

THE MONKEY AND THE PEAS

A monkey was carrying two handfuls of peas. One little pea dropped out. He tried to pick it up, and spilled twenty. He tried to pick up the twenty, and spilled them all. Then he lost his temper, scattered the peas in all directions, and ran away.

Leo Tolstoy.

ARTHUR'S FIRST NIGHT AT RUGBY

By Thomas Hughes

Rugby is one of the great schools of England. It is situated in a town of the same name in Warwickshire, near Birmingham. Thomas Arnold, who served there from 1828 to 1842, was its most celebrated head master. Thomas Hughes, who wrote *Tom Brown's School Days*, from which the incident below is taken, was educated at Rugby under Doctor Arnold.

The little fellows went quietly to their own beds and began undressing and talking to one another in whispers, while the elder boys, among whom was Tom, sat about chatting on one another's beds, with their jackets and waistcoats off.

Poor little Arthur was overcome with the strangeness of his position. The idea of sleeping in the room with strange boys had clearly never crossed his mind before, and was as painful as it was strange to him. He could hardly bear to take his jacket off. However, presently with an effort, off it came, and then he paused and looked at Tom, who was sitting at the bottom of his bed, talking and laughing.

"Please, Brown," he whispered, "may I wash my face and hands?"

"Of course, if you like," said Tom, staring. "That's your wash-hand stand, under the window, second from your bed. You'll have to go down for more water in the morning if you use it all."

And on he went with his talk, while Arthur stole timidly from between the beds out to his wash-stand, and began to bathe, thereby drawing for a moment on himself the attention of the room.

On went the talk and laughter. Arthur finished his washing and undressing and put on his night-gown. He then looked round more nervously than ever. Two or three of the little boys were already in bed, sitting up with their chins on their knees. The light burned clear; the noise went on.

It was a trying moment for the poor little lonely boy. However, this time he didn't ask Tom what he might or might not do, but dropped on his knees by his bedside, as he had done every day from his childhood.

Tom was sitting at the bottom of his bed unlacing his boots, so that his back was toward Arthur, and he didn't see what had happened, and looked up in wonder at the sudden silence. Then two or three boys laughed and sneered, and a big, brutal fellow, who was standing in the middle of the room, picked up a slipper and shied it at the kneeling boy. Then Tom saw the whole, and the next moment the boot he had just pulled off, flew straight at the head of the bully, who had just time to throw up his arm and catch it on his elbow.

"Confound you, Brown, what's that for?" roared he, stamping with pain.

"Never mind what I mean," said Tom, stepping on to

the floor, every drop of blood in his body tingling; "if any fellow wants the other boot, he knows how to get it."

What would have been the result is doubtful, for at this moment the sixth-form boy came in, and not another word could be said. Tom and the others rushed into bed and finished their unrobing there, and the janitor had put out the candle in another minute, and toddled on to the next room, shutting the door with his usual, "Good night, gen'l'm'n."

There were many boys in the room by whom that little scene was taken to heart before they slept. But sleep seemed to have deserted the pillow of poor Tom. For some time his excitement and the flood of memories which chased one another through his brain, kept him from thinking. His head throbbed, his heart leaped, and he could hardly keep himself from springing out of bed and rushing about the room.

Then the thought of his own mother came across him, and the promise he had made at her knee, years ago, never to forget to kneel by his bedside and give himself up to his Father before he laid his head on the pillow, from which it might never rise. He lay down gently, and cried as if his heart would break. He was only fourteen years old.

When Tom first came to the school he did not kneel down because of the noise, but sat up in bed till the candle was out, and then stole out and said his prayers, in fear lest some one should find him out. So did many another poor little fellow.

Then he began to think that he might just as well say his prayers in bed, and then, that it did not matter whether he was kneeling, or sitting, or lying down. For the last year he had probably not said his prayers in earnest a dozen times.

Poor Tom! the first and bitterest feeling which was like to break his heart, was the sense of his own cowardice. How could he bear it? And then the poor, little, weak boy, whom he had pitied and almost scorned for his weakness, had done that which he, braggart as he was, dared not do.

The first dawn of comfort came to him in vowing to himself that he would stand by that boy through thick and thin, and cheer him, and help him, and bear his burdens, for the good deed done that night. Then he resolved to write home next day and tell his mother all, and what a coward her son had been. And then peace came to him as he resolved, lastly, to bear his testimony next morning.

Next morning he was up and washed and dressed, all but his jacket and waistcoat, just as the ten minutes' bell began to ring, and then in the face of the whole room he knelt down to pray. Not five words could he say, —the bell mocked him; he was listening to every whisper in the room,—what were they all thinking of him?

He was ashamed to go on kneeling, ashamed to rise from his knees. At last, as it were from his inmost heart, a still, small voice seemed to breathe forth the words of the publican, " God be merciful to me a sinner!" He repeated them over and over, clinging to them as for his life, and rose from his knees comforted and humbled, and ready to face the whole world. It was not needed. Two other boys besides Arthur had already followed his example, and he went down to the great school with a glimmering of another lesson in his heart—the lesson that he who has conquered his own coward spirit has conquered the whole outward world.

He found, too, how greatly he had exaggerated the effect to be produced by his act. For a few nights there was a sneer or a laugh when he knelt down, but this passed off soon, and one by one all the other boys but three or four followed the lead.

From "Tom Brown's School Days."

God that madest Earth and Heaven,
  Darkness and light!
Who the day for toil hast given,
  For rest the night!
May Thine angel guards defend us,
Slumber sweet Thy mercy send us,
Holy dreams and hopes attend us,
  This livelong night!

Reginald Heber.

THE VILLAGE BLACKSMITH

By Henry Wadsworth Longfellow

In the pleasant town of Portland, Maine, in the fine old house of his uncle, a well-to-do sea-captain, Henry Wadsworth Longfellow

was born in 1807. There were four brothers and four sisters in the family, with books and music and games to keep them busy and happy. In the evenings they would gather around a big table to study their lessons. When these were mastered, the room would often be cleared, and they would have a merry time practising the steps they had learned at dancing school to the tune of *Money Musk* or *The Sailor's Hornpipe*.

On Sunday, Henry went twice to meeting, often in winter carrying his mother's little foot-stove of coals and in summer a cluster of pinks or apple blossoms from the garden. When he first went to school he was borne on horseback in front of the negro who worked for his father. He learned easily and read much. "Every reader," he afterward wrote, "has his first book; I mean to say, one book among all others which in early youth first fascinates his imagination, and at once excites and satisfies the desires of his mind. For me, this first book was the *Sketch-Book* of Washington Irving. I was a school-boy when it was published, and read each succeeding number with ever-increasing wonder and delight, spellbound by its pleasant humor, its melancholy tenderness, its atmosphere of reverie,—nay, even by its gray-brown covers, the shaded letters of its titles, and the fair clear type." Their summers the Longfellow children spent on a farm a few miles out of Portland with their grandfather, a stately old man wearing a cocked hat and his hair tied by a black ribbon. This grandfather would tell them how he was once captured by the British, and of his adventures in escaping. One day when Henry was thirteen, he slipped quietly out of the house, and running down the street, poked an envelope in the letter-box of the semi-weekly newspaper. On the day when the paper appeared he and his sister—the only person who knew his secret—could scarcely wait until their father allowed them to take it. Yes, there they were in the corner—unsigned—the first verses of Henry Wadsworth Longfellow. His happy boyhood in Portland, Longfellow describes in his poem *My Lost Youth:*

> I remember the black wharves and the slips,
> And the sea-tides tossing free;
> And Spanish sailors with bearded lips,
> And the beauty and mystery of the ships,
> And the magic of the sea.
> And the voice of that wayward song
> Is singing and saying still,
> "A boy's will is the wind's will,
> And the thoughts of youth are long, long thoughts."

When Longfellow was older he studied both at Bowdoin College and at Harvard University. Later, after traveling abroad, he taught, first at Bowdoin and then at Harvard. Famous old Craigie House in Cambridge, which had been Washington's headquarters during the siege of Boston became more famous as the home of the poet Longfellow. Longfellow was honored by degrees from both Oxford and Cambridge Universities, in England, and by a bust in the Poets' Corner in Westminster Abbey. On his seventy-second birthday the public school children of Cambridge gave him an arm-chair made of the wood of the horse-chestnut tree beneath which the "village smithy" of the town, celebrated in the following poem, had once stood. Longfellow died in 1882.

4—4th

Under a spreading chestnut-tree
    The village smithy stands;
The smith, a mighty man is he,
    With large and sinewy hands;
And the muscles of his brawny arms
    Are strong as iron bands.

His hair is crisp, and black, and long,
    Ilis face is like the tan;
His brow is wet with honest sweat,
    He earns whate'er he can,
And looks the whole world in the face,
    For he owes not any man.

Week in, week out, from morn till night,
    You can hear his bellows blow;
You can hear him swing his heavy sledge,
    With measured beat and slow,
Like a sexton ringing the village bell,
    When the evening sun is low.

And children coming home from school
    Look in at the open door;
They love to see the flaming forge,
    And hear the bellows roar,
And catch the burning sparks that fly
    Like chaff from a threshing-floor.

He goes on Sunday to the church,
    And sits among his boys;
He hears the parson pray and preach,
    He hears his daughter's voice,
Singing in the village choir,
    And it makes his heart rejoice.

It sounds to him like her mother's voice,
    Singing in Paradise!
He needs must think of her once more,
    How in the grave she lies;
And with his hard, rough hand he wipes
    A tear out of his eyes.

Toiling,—rejoicing,—sorrowing,
    Onward through life he goes;
Each morning sees some task begin,
    Each evening sees it close;
Something attempted, something done,
    Has earned a night's repose.

Thanks, thanks to thee, my worthy friend,
    For the lesson thou hast taught!
Thus at the flaming forge of life
    Our fortunes must be wrought;
Thus on its sounding anvil shaped
    Each burning deed and thought.

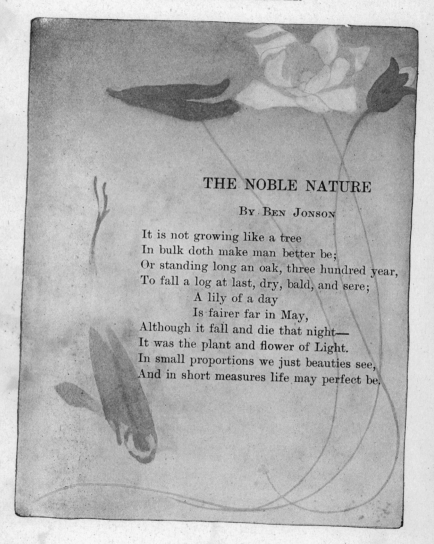

THE NOBLE NATURE

By Ben Jonson

It is not growing like a tree
In bulk doth make man better be;
Or standing long an oak, three hundred year,
To fall a log at last, dry, bald, and sere;
    A lily of a day
    Is fairer far in May,
Although it fall and die that night—
It was the plant and flower of Light.
In small proportions we just beauties see,
And in short measures life may perfect be.

SOME PROVERBS OF KING SOLOMON

A soft answer turneth away wrath: but grievous words stir up anger.

The eyes of the Lord are in every place, beholding the evil and the good.

Better is a little with righteousness, than great revenues without right.

Pride goeth before destruction, and an haughty spirit before a fall.

He that is slow to anger is better than the mighty; and he that ruleth his spirit than he that taketh a city.

Even a child is known by his doings, whether his work be pure, and whether it be right.

A good name is rather to be chosen than great riches, and loving favor rather than silver and gold.

Seest thou a man diligent in his business? he shall stand before kings; he shall not stand before mean men.

Apply thine heart unto instruction, and thine ears to the words of knowledge.

Buy the truth, and sell it not; also wisdom, and instruction, and understanding.

A word fitly spoken is like apples of gold in pictures of silver.

A friend loveth at all times, and a brother is born for adversity.

From " The Bible."

THE REVERIE OF POOR SUSAN

By WILLIAM WORDSWORTH

At the corner of Wood Street, when daylight appears,
Hangs a Thrush that sings loud, it has sung for three
      years:
Poor Susan has passed by the spot, and has heard
In the silence of morning the song of the Bird.

'Tis a note of enchantment; what ails her?   She sees
A mountain ascending, a vision of trees;
Bright volumes of vapor through Lothbury glide,
And a river flows on through the vale of Cheapside.

Green pastures she views in the midst of the dale,
Down which she so often has tripped with her pail;
And a single small cottage, a nest like a dove's,
The one only dwelling on earth that she loves.

She looks, and her heart is in heaven: but they fade,
The mist and the river, the hill and the shade:
The stream will not flow, and the hill will not rise,
And the colors have all passed away from her eyes!

———————

Small service is true service while it lasts.

William Wordsworth.

THE HOUSE IN BIDWELL STREET

By George Ade

I am one of a large family. We stand in a row along Bidwell Street. When first I had any knowledge of myself I was a mere skeleton framework of scantling. There were six of us, just alike, and we were knee-deep in bright yellow lumber.

All day long the workmen crawled over our ribs. I felt the rap-a-tap-tap as I became decently clad in weatherboarding and shingles. They shouldered the clean, sweet-smelling pine through every gaping door and window.

At last I was a completed house with the brass knobs glittering and the raw wood hidden under two glossy colors of paint.

The shavings and litter were carried away. Tufts of green grass began to show in the trampled front yard. To be sure I had a sort of damp feeling in my joints and was still untidy with the siftings of sawdust and the splatterings of paint and plastering, but I had the pride of knowing that I was as handsome as any other house in Bidwell Street.

Since then I have learned by eavesdropping that Bidwell Street is supposed to be a shabby and uncounted thoroughfare and that our sextette is not in the fashion. One day a very gay little house, with scalloped decorations fastened to it, came along Bidwell Street on rollers and I remember that it was very reluctant to take up with our society, and had to be dragged a few feet at a time.

Sometimes, by lifting myself and peeping, I can see the bulky shapes of large buildings far away. They are behind clouds of smoke and I do not envy them their largeness. In fact I envy no other house, for contentment has come to me.

For a time I was inwardly troubled. The first blow to my pride came soon after the painters had given me the last finishing caress.

A man and a woman stopped in front of me and stared critically. The woman said, "Dear me!" in a tone of such disappointment that I felt a tremor in every rafter. They unlocked the front door and walked through the rooms, their footfalls starting the hollow echoes, and the woman found fault with me. The man said they would have to take me, with all my imperfections.

The two were childless and out of luck, and they seemed to regard me as a place of exile, so how was I to cheer them when they always wore a frown for me? I had hoped to be loved, but I was merely tolerated. Still, I was rather glad they came. I will admit that it felt good to get the carpets and rugs and shiny furniture and looped curtains; for a house, after being well furnished, has the same satisfaction that a man has after he has dined properly.

The inner warmth drove away the lingering chill and damp, and it was certainly pleasanter to glow with lamps than to stand lonesomely in the darkness.

Yet I was constantly saddened by the thought that those whom I held and sheltered, and gathered under my warm plastering, even as a hen gathers her brood, did not think well of me.

The woman used to have an occasional caller, to whom she would apologize for my poor dimensions (think of it!), and she would say that the neighborhood was unattractive. I will confess that I was indignant.

Leaving my own merits out of the question, there is certainly no excuse for saying evil things of Bidwell Street. The men work for their money and the women love their children. And such children! I have seen the street white with them on a Sunday evening, for every little girl had a white dress and every boy a white waist. The men sat in the open air and smoked. The women called gaily from door-step to door-step, and the children fluttered everywhere like sparrows. It has seemed to me on such a night, that I would rather be here in Bidwell Street than anywhere else.

When the unhappy couple moved out one day in early spring I did not care so much, although that night I had to stand in conspicuous gloom and feel the sweep of cold drafts. The woman said she hoped she would never see me again, but the man, as I believe, did not feel so un-

kindly toward me. The wagons disappeared down the
street, but wherever they stopped, I don't believe that house
will be a home for the man.

After my first family went away there followed a cheer-
less month. Company is company, even though it offend
you. I had the feeling of being neglected when I saw the
smoke curl from other chimneys and heard the children
shouting before the houses across the way.

But one day—and I must always call it the best of days
—a pudgy, red-faced little man stopped squarely in front
of me and said, "Oho!"

I think all of my front panes must have crinkled back
a smile at him, for I liked this little man.

Then there came into view a plump woman with two
red spots on her cheeks, and a little boy who had his mother's cheeks and his father's wrinkly eyes, and two very
small girls with braided hair, who hopped and skipped like
springy little frogs.

"Is it the place, Henry?" asked the woman.

"Yes—see," he replied, pointing to my number.

"Isn't it fine? All this nice grass in front."

"But behind!" exclaimed Henry. "Ah, behind—for a
garden—big—plenty of room!"

"Is this where we're going to live?" shouted the boy,
dancing on the front stoop.

"Maybe—yes," replied the father, laughing. Then the
boy laughed and the mother laughed and the two little

girls laughed, and for the first time I wanted to laugh too, although it was utterly preposterous for a house to expect to laugh.

That day, within the hour, my self-respect came back and I fear I was almost as vain as I was on the day when the painters got through with me.

The laughing family said my rooms were the prettiest in the world, my closets the snuggest and my kitchen the tidiest.

So I knew they were coming back, and they did come, with some of the queerest bales and chests and bundles that I had ever seen on a wagon in Bidwell Street. The furniture was new, but the bales and chests and bundles had come from the old country, and, being unpacked, they brought forth strange dishes, cutlery, pictures, clothing, bedding and the like, all cumbersome and showing service, but mightily homelike.

Once more I felt my rafters warmed, and once more the light from my windows fell across the sidewalk where the young women and their sweethearts promenaded slowly each pleasant evening.

The new family loved me! So, of course, I had to love the new family, because a real home always tries to multiply the affection brought into it.

Summer was coming. Now the open windows were filled with plants, and the grass spread over the front yard, covering the bare spots. The whole family went gardening in the back yard, and there was such shouting and laughing at work that all the work was like play.

I came to know the family secrets. In the old country the little man had been poor and the family lived in two rooms, and did not have meat oftener than once a week. They would tell of the old country sometimes, and when they sat down to eat the wife would say: "Oh, Henry, in the old country this would be a holiday feast."

What a stroke of fortune to be found by these people, who could delight in having a house of their own with a garden at the back and the vines beginning to climb in front!

No wonder I was proud. They said the best things about me, and wrote about me to their friends in the old country, and they even had me photographed. That day I squared up and looked my best, for I could not remember that any other house in Bidwell Street had been photographed.

Through fall and winter they kept me warmed with their simple goodness, and I was so grateful that on windy nights I would soothe the children to sleep. When the wind whistled at my eaves I would change the whistle to a crooning sound, which none but the children could understand, and which is never heard except where there are children to listen.

The three would lie in their beds and listen to the droning lullaby, and soon all three would go to sleep smiling.

They thought it was the wind singing to them, but I did my part, for I am sure the song did not sound the same at any other house in Bidwell Street.

Spring and summer came again. The vines hung in showers of green around the front windows and the children sang in the street.

One morning I drowsed in greater happiness than usual, for now there were four children instead of three.

Such bantering as they had! He said it was his and she said it was hers, and I longed to speak up and say it was mine also.

It is winter now. The fourth one sits strapped at the window and laughs at the children outside.

I believe I am the proudest house in Bidwell Street.

OUT TO OLD AUNT MARY'S

By James Whitcomb Riley

Wasn't it pleasant, O brother mine,
In those old days of the lost sunshine
   Of youth—when the Saturday's chores were
      through,
   And the "Sunday's wood" in the kitchen, too,
   And we went visiting, "me and you,"
      Out to old Aunt Mary's?—

It all comes back so clear to-day!
Though I am as bald as you are gray,—
    Out by the barn-lot and down the lane
    We patter along in the dust again,
    As light as the tips of the drops of the rain,
      Out to old Aunt Mary's.

The few last houses of the town;
Then on, up the high creek-bluffs and down;
    Past the squat tollgate, with its well-sweep pole;
    The bridge, and "the old Babtizin'-hole,"
    Loitering, awed, o'er pool and shoal,
      Out to old Aunt Mary's.

We cross the pasture, and through the wood,
Where the old gray snag of the poplar stood,
    Where the hammering "red-heads" hopped awry,
    And the buzzard "raised" in the clearing sky
    And lolled and circled, as we went by
      Out to old Aunt Mary's.

Or, stayed by the glint of the redbird's wings,
Or the glitter of song that the bluebird sings,
    All hushed we feign to strike strange trails,
    As the "big braves" do in the Indian tales,
    Till again our real quest lags and fails—
      Out to old Aunt Mary's.—

And the woodland echoes with yells of mirth
That make old war-whoops of minor worth!
   Where such heroes of war as we?—
   With bows and arrows of fantasy,
   Chasing each other from tree to tree
     Out to old Aunt Mary's!

And then in the dust of the road again;
And the teams we met, and the countrymen;
   And the long highway, with sunshine spread
   As thick as butter on country bread,
   Our cares behind, and our hearts ahead
    Out to old Aunt Mary's.—

For only, now, at the road's next bend
To the right we could make out the gable-end
   Of the fine old Huston homestead—not
   Half a mile from the sacred spot
   Where dwelt our Saint in her simple cot—
    Out to old Aunt Mary's.

Far fields, bottom-lands, creek-banks—all,
We ranged at will.—Where the waterfall
   Laughed all day as it slowly poured
   Over the dam by the old mill-ford,
   While the tail-race writhed, and the mill-wheel
    roared—
    Out to old Aunt Mary's.

For, O my brother so far away,
This is to tell you—she waits *to-day*
   To welcome us :—Aunt Mary fell
   Asleep this morning, whispering, " Tell
   The boys to come " . . . And all is well
    "Out to old Aunt Mary's."

                        Abridged.

HANS, CLODHOPPER

RETOLD FROM HANS CHRISTIAN ANDERSEN

SCENE I

The courtyard of a country mansion near Nonsense Land in the latter part of the fifteenth century. The Princess of the country has promised to marry the man who can speak best for himself and has appointed a day on which suitors may present themselves.

Enter father with Peter and Klaus gorgeously dressed and with whips in their hands. Two servants follow leading horses.

Father. The white horse is for thee, son Peter; the black horse is thine, Klaus. Art ready, my sons, to go to win the Princess?

Peter and Klaus. (*Cracking their whips.*) Ay! ay! father.

Father. The time was short, what hast thou ready to say for thyselves?

Peter. (*Hurriedly.*) I'm sure on it, father! I'm sure on it! (*Slaps his knee.*) Dost think any one can say more than the town newspapers for three years, forwards and backwards?

Klaus. (*Breaks in.*) Newspapers are but the vulgar tongue of the people! 'Tis I who can address the Princess with propriety. Harken! the Latin dictionary! (*Recites in monotone.*) *Ab-dō,-didī,-ditum; ab-nuō,-nuī,-nuitum; ab-oleō,-ēvī,-itum.* (*Enter Hans running.*)

Hans. Where art thou going with all thy fine clothes?

Klaus. Thou hast nothing to do with it! Now I must begin again. *Ab-dō̄,-didī,-ditum ; ab-nuŏ,-nuī,-nui-tum.*

Father. (*Interrupts proudly.*) That is enough, son Klaus. Thou art well prepared. Be off! Good luck! The Princess must needs take one of you.

(*Peter and Klaus ride gaily away.*)

Hans. The Princess! Father, give me a horse! I wish to be married, too! If she takes me, she takes me, and if she doesn't take me I shall take her all the same.

Father. Stuff and nonsense! Thou art but a clod-hopper. I will give thee no horse. Thou hast nothing to say for thyself. Now, thy brothers are fine fellows.

Hans. If I mayn't have a horse, I'll take the billy-goat. He is my own and he can carry me very well! (*Seats himself on the billy-goat, digs his heels into its sides and gallops down the road.*)

SCENE II

On the road. Enter Peter and Klaus riding slowly along, each talking to himself as if reciting.

Hans comes at a gallop!

Hans. Here I come! Tra-la-la-la-la-la! (*Peter and Klaus ride on in silence.*) Here I come, I say! See what I found on the road! (*Holds up a crow that he has killed.*)

"I SHALL GIVE IT TO THE KING'S DAUGHTER"

Klaus. What in the world will you do with that, Clodhopper?

Hans. I shall give it to the king's daughter.

Peter. (*Laughing.*) Yes, I would do that.

Hans. And see what else I have found! One doesn't find such a thing as this every day on the road! (*Holds up an old wooden shoe.*)

Klaus. (*Takes the shoe and looks it over carefully.*) Is the Princess to have this, too?

Hans. Yes, indeed, she is! And this, too! (*Puts his hand in his pocket and brings out some sand.*)

Peter. (*Laughing.*) Now, that is the best of all! Sand scooped out of the ditch!

Hans. Yes, that it is! See, my pockets are full of it!

Klaus. Stay thou here! We'll not be disgraced by such as thee. (*Peter and Klaus gallop away.*)

Hans. I'll not stay here. I'm as good as they. (*Digs his heels into his billy-goat and rides furiously after them.*)

SCENE III

The next day. The throne room in the castle. The ceiling is of looking-glass, so that each suitor sees himself walking on his head as he crosses the creaking floor to the dais on which is seated the Princess. The room is unbearably hot. At the windows sit three clerks, who write down what each applicant has to say for himself. Marching solemnly up and down is a pompous alderman, who is master of ceremonies. Outside are seen the suitors standing in line as tight as may be to keep them from tearing off one another's clothes in jealousy. Curious heads bob up from time to time and peer through the windows to see the successive unfortunates.

The Princess. (*To a sheepish looking fellow who can not open his mouth.*) Bah! Away with him! (*Enter Klaus, who glances at the ceiling and becomes dizzy.*)

The Princess. Is it too hot in here for thee?

Klaus. (*Trembling.*) *Ab—dō—didī—ditum.*

The Princess. The man is mad! Away with him! (*Enter Peter, whose knees fairly knock together.*)

The Princess. Is it too hot in here for thee?

Peter. I—i—it is t—t—terribly h—h—hot in here.

The Princess. That is because my father is roasting cockerels to-day.

Peter. P—p—p—p— (*Snaps his fingers.*) P—p— p—p—

The Princess. What a simpleton! Away with him!

Hans. (*Hans rides his billy-goat straight into the room and speaks before the Princess can open her mouth.*) What a burning heat you have here!

The Princess. That is because my father is roasting cockerels to-day.

Hans. How convenient! I suppose I can get a crow roasted, too.

The Princess. Yes, very well. But have you anything to roast it in? I have neither pot nor pan.

Hans. But I have. Here is a cooking-pot. (*Brings out the wooden shoe and puts the crow into it.*)

The Princess. Why, you have enough for a whole meal. But where shall we get any dripping to baste it with?

Hans. Oh, I have some in my pocket. I have enough and to spare. (*Pours a little of the sand out of his pocket.*)

The Princess. Now I like that. You have an answer for everything and you have something to say for yourself. I will have you for a husband. But do you know that every word we have said will be in the alderman's paper to-morrow? (*Alderman and clerks hold their sides with laughter.*)

Hans. Ah! That is just the thing! He can publish the banns. (*Rides across the room to the alderman.*) My gracious, revered and august lord, pray accept this crow in token of the appreciation of Her Loveliness and my humble self. We shall be married at high noon to-morrow. (*Kisses his hand to the Princess and tears out of the room.*)

———————

Peter Piper picked a peck of pickled pepper;
A peck of pickled pepper Peter Piper picked;
If Peter Piper picked a peck of pickled pepper,
Where's the peck of pickled pepper Peter Piper picked?

THE GRAY SWAN

By Alice Cary

"Oh tell me, sailor, tell me true,
Is my little lad, my Elihu,
    A-sailing with your ship?"
The sailor's eyes were dim with dew,—
"Your little lad, your Elihu?"
    He said, with trembling lip,—
    "What little lad? what ship?"

"What little lad! as if there could be
Another such an one as he!
    What little lad, do you say?
Why, Elihu, that took to the sea
The moment I put him off my knee!
    It was just the other day
    The *Gray Swan* sailed away."

"The other day?" The sailor's eyes
Stood open with a great surprise,—
    "The other day? the *Swan?*"
His heart began in his throat to rise.
"Ay, ay, sir, here in the cupboard lies
    The jacket he had on."
    "And so your lad is gone?"

"Gone with the *Swan*."   "And did she stand
  With her anchor clutching hold of the sand,
    For a month, and never stir?"
"Why, to be sure!   I've seen from the land,
  Like a lover kissing his lady's hand,
    The wild sea kissing her,—
    A sight to remember, sir."

"But, my good mother, do you know
  All this was twenty years ago?
    I stood on the *Gray Swan's* deck,
And to that lad I saw you throw,
Taking it off, as it might be, so!
    The kerchief from your neck."
    "Ay, and he'll bring it back!"

"And did the little lawless lad
  That has made you sick and made you sad,
    Sail with the *Gray Swan's* crew?"
"Lawless! the man is going mad!
  The best boy ever mother had,
    Be sure he sailed with the crew!
    What would you have him do?"

"And he has never written line,
  Nor sent you word, nor made you sign
    To say he was alive?"

"Hold! if 'twas wrong, the wrong is mine;
Besides, he may be in the brine,
    And could he write from the grave?
    Tut, man! what would you have?"

"Gone twenty years,—a long, long cruise,—
'Twas wicked thus your love to abuse;
    But if the lad still live,
And come back home, think you you can
Forgive him?"—"Miserable man,
    You're mad as the sea,—you rave,—
    What have I to forgive?"

The sailor twitched his shirt so blue,
And from within his bosom drew
    The kerchief.   She was wild.
"My God! my Father! is it true?
My little lad, my Elihu
    My blessed boy, my child!
    My dead, my living child!"

Stay, stay at home, my heart, and rest;
Home-keeping hearts are happiest,
    For those that wander they know not where
    Are full of trouble and full of care,
To stay at home is best.
    From "Song."   *Henry Wadsworth Longfellow.*

THE LAST ROSE OF SUMMER

By Thomas Moore

'Tis the last rose of Summer
  Left blooming alone;
All her lovely companions
  Are faded and gone;
No flower of her kindred,
  No rosebud is nigh,
To reflect back her blushes,
  Or give sigh for sigh!

I'll not leave thee, thou lone one,
  To pine on the stem;
Since the lovely are sleeping,
  Go, sleep thou with them.
Thus kindly I scatter
  Thy leaves o'er the bed
Where thy mates of the garden
  Lie scentless and dead.

Abridged

THE MERRY PRANKS OF TILL OWLGLASS

From the German

In the fourteenth century there lived in northern Germany a mischievous fellow by the name of Till Owlglass. He traveled from country to country and grew so famous for his merry pranks that he became known even at court.

One morning as he was strolling through a large city, he saw a sign painter putting fresh figures on a sun-dial, which had been washed off by the rain.

"How often must that be done?" inquired Owlglass.

"Every year," replied the painter.

"That is a great waste," said Owlglass. "Why don't your townspeople build a roof over your sun-dial?"

"You are right," said the painter. "I will tell the mayor."

The mayor was so pleased with this advice, that he sent for Owlglass, thanked him and gave him two bright silver dollars. He also gave orders to have a roof built over the sun-dial at once. But alas! when the roof was finished the citizens found to their sorrow that although protected from the rain, the sun-dial was now always in shadow.

Till journeyed on until he reached the North Sea. While walking along the shore he saw a party of men bathing. Suddenly one of them cried: "Wait, friends, and let me count to see if we are all here. One of our number seems to be missing." So he began and counted right, but forgot to count himself. At this he was overcome with fright and said: "We were nine, one must be drowned!"

"Let me count," said another, but he forgot to count himself just as the first one had done. The swimmers now felt sure that one of their number must be drowned and they swam sorrowfully to the shore. As they stood bewailing their loss, Till asked them what the trouble was.

"Oh, sir!" they cried, "we were nine, and now we are only eight. One of us must be drowned, but we can not tell which."

"I can readily solve the riddle," said Owlglass. "Lie down every one of you and stick your noses into the sand!" This they did.

"Now stand up," continued he.

They rose as one man.

"Now count the dents in the sand. So many dents, so many noses, so many men."

They counted and gave a shout of joy.

"Hurrah!" cried they, "nine dents, nine noses, nine men. There is no one drowned!"

Thanking Till for his help, they went joyfully home and Owlglass resumed his pilgrimage.

Not long after, the king stood at a window of the palace and gazed with pride upon the soldiers, assembled before the castle.   They were all armed and equipped for battle.   Owlglass stepped up to the king and asked where they were going.

"They are going to war," replied the king.

"And what will they do there?" asked Owlglass.

"They will destroy fields and orchards, burn and plunder villages, pursue and kill the enemy," said the king.

"For what purpose?" continued Till.

"So that peace may be restored, you simpleton!" exclaimed the king.

"Would it not be better to arrange for peace before the battle and avoid all this bloodshed?" asked Till.

"You are right!" cried the king, and at once sent messengers to arrange a treaty of peace.   So Owlglass was the means of saving many lives, and instead of having a war, the king gave a festival in honor of peace.

Going on, Till met the archbishop.   "Tell me, what is your trade?" asked the archbishop.

"I am a spectacle maker," said Till, "and give people glasses through which to study the world, but lately there has been little demand for my spectacles, for those in authority look at the world through their fingers.   They spend their time trying to win grace and favor rather than trying to study the difference between right and wrong in order to deal justly by every one."   The archbishop was so pleased with Till's little sermon that he invited him to come and live at court.   Abridged.

EVENING AT THE FARM

By John Townsend Trowbridge

Over the hill the farm-boy goes.
His shadow lengthens along the land,
A giant staff in a giant hand;
In the poplar-tree, above the spring,
The katydid begins to sing;
　　The early dews are falling;—
Into the stone-heap darts the mink;
The swallows skim the river's brink;
And home to the woodland fly the crows,
When over the hill the farm-boy goes,
　　Cheerily calling,
　　"Co', boss! co', boss! co'! co'! co'!"
Farther, farther, over the hill,
Faintly calling, calling still,
　　"Co', boss! co', boss! co'! co'!"

Now to her task the milkmaid goes.
The cattle come crowding through the gate,
Lowing, pushing, little and great;
About the trough, by the farm-yard pump,
The frolicsome yearlings frisk and jump,
　　While the pleasant dews are falling;—
The new milch heifer is quick and shy,
But the old cow waits with tranquil eye,

And the white stream into the bright pail flows,
When to her task the milkmaid goes,
  Soothingly calling,
 "So, boss! so, boss! so! so! so!"
The cheerful milkmaid takes her stool,
And sits and milks in the twilight cool,
  Saying, "So! so, boss! so! so!"

To supper at last the farmer goes.
The apples are pared, the paper read,
The stories are told, then all to bed.
Without, the crickets' ceaseless song
Makes shrill the silence all night long;
  The heavy dews are falling.
The housewife's hand has turned the lock;
Drowsily ticks the kitchen clock;
The household sinks to deep repose,
But still in sleep the farm-boy goes,
  Singing, calling,—
 "Co', boss! co', boss! co'! co'! co'!"
And oft the milkmaid, in her dreams,
Drums in the pail with the flashing streams,
  Murmuring, "So, boss! so!"

Abridged.

Now came still evening on, and Twilight gray
Had in her sober livery all things clad.

From "Paradise Lost." John Milton.

PREPARING FOR CHRISTMAS

BY LOUISA M. ALCOTT

The life of Louisa M. Alcott was that of a brave, active woman who seems never to have thought of herself or her own needs.   Her

early years in Boston and Concord were full of poverty and hardship, and yet they were happy years, too.   The four Alcott children ate their rice without sugar and their corn meal without molasses.   In Boston, Louisa liked to roll her hoop around the common before breakfast.   She could "climb a tree like a squirrel", and beat her boy friends racing.   The children had delightful playmates in the little Emersons and Hawthornes.   In the old empty barn at the foot of the garden they had fine times acting plays.   At first they chose *Jack the Giant Killer* and *Cinderella*, but later Louisa wrote to a friend, "I like tragic plays, and shall be a Siddons if I can.   We get up harps, dresses, waterfalls and thunder, and have great fun."   Of these good times Miss Alcott has told us in her stories, especially in *Little Women*, which reflects much of her home life.   Bronson Alcott, Louisa's father, was a famous teacher and writer, and there was much wise talk at the family table.   Each child was made to keep a journal faithfully, and so Louisa early learned to write.   The Alcott home was a refuge for the poor and the distressed.   Once Mrs. Alcott hid a runaway slave in a brick oven.   Louisa's dearest wish at this time was that she might grow up to make money so that her father and mother would be comfortable.   At sixteen she was already helping, teaching school, writing stories, and at night, sewing. One summer vacation she spent as a servant, and did washing. But the publishers began to like her work and ask for more. With good pay came easier times. *Little Women* she called. "The first golden egg of the ugly duckling," for it made her fortune. A million copies of her books were sold, making her name a household word, and bringing her many thousands of dollars. During the Civil War, Miss Alcott nursed the sick and wounded. She died at fifty-six, in 1888, two days after the death of her father.

The clock struck six; and Beth, having swept up the hearth, put a pair of slippers down to warm. Somehow, the sight of the old shoes had a good effect upon the girls, for mother was coming home, and every one brightened to welcome her. Meg stopped lecturing, and lit the lamp. Amy got out of the easy-chair without being asked, and Jo forgot how tired she was, as she sat up to hold the slippers nearer the blaze.

"They are quite worn out; mother must have a new pair."

"I thought I'd get her some with my dollar," said Beth.

"No, I shall!" cried Amy.

"I'm the oldest," began Meg, but Jo cut in with a decided—

"I'm the man of the family, now papa is away, and I shall provide the slippers, for he told me to take special care of mother while he was gone."

"I'll tell you what we'll do," said Beth, "let's each get

6—4th

her something for Christmas, and not get anything for ourselves."

"That's like you, dear! What shall we get!" exclaimed Jo.

Every one thought soberly for a minute; then Meg announced, as if the idea was suggested by the sight of her own pretty hands, "I shall give her a nice pair of gloves."

"Army shoes, best to be had," cried Jo.

"Some handkerchiefs, all hemmed," said Beth.

"I'll get a little bottle of cologne; she likes it, and it won't cost much, so I'll have some left to buy something for me," added Amy.

"How shall we give the things?" asked Meg.

"Put them on the table, and bring her in and see her open the bundles. Don't you remember how we used to do on our birthdays?" answered Jo.

"I used to be so frightened when it was my turn to sit in the big chair with a crown on, and see you all come marching round to give the presents, with a kiss. I liked the things and the kisses, but it was dreadful to have you sit looking at me while I opened the bundles," said Beth, who was toasting her face and the bread for tea, at the same time.

"Let mother think we are getting things for ourselves, and then surprise her. We must go shopping to-morrow afternoon, Meg; there is lots to do about the play for

Christmas night," said Jo, marching up and down with her hands behind her back, and her nose in the air.

"I don't mean to act any more after this time; I'm getting too old for such things," observed Meg, who was as much a child as ever about "dressing-up" frolics.

"You won't stop, I know, as long as you can trail round in a white gown with your hair down, and wear gold-paper jewelry. You are the best actress we have, and there'll be an end of everything if you quit the boards," said Jo. "We ought to rehearse to-night; come here, Amy, and do the fainting scene, for you are as stiff as a poker in that."

"I can't help it; I never saw any one faint, and I don't choose to make myself all black and blue, tumbling flat, as you do. If I can go down easily, I'll drop; if I can't, I shall fall into a chair and be graceful—I don't care if Hugo does come at me with a pistol," returned Amy, who was not gifted with dramatic power, but was chosen because she was small enough to be borne out, shrieking, by the hero of the piece.

"Do it this way; clasp your hands so, and then stagger across the room, crying frantically, 'Roderigo! save me! save me!'" and away went Jo, with a melodramatic scream which was truly thrilling.

Amy followed, but she poked her hands out stiffly before her, and jerked herself along as if she went by machinery; and her "Ow" was more suggestive of pins being run into her than of fear and anguish. Jo gave a despairing groan, and Meg laughed outright, while Beth let her bread burn as she watched the fun with interest.

"It's no use! do the best you can when the time comes, and if the audience shout, don't blame me. Come on, Meg."

Then things went smoothly, for Don Pedro defied the world in a speech of two pages without a single break; Hagar, the witch, chanted an awful incantation over her kettleful of simmering toads with weird effect; Roderigo rent his chains asunder manfully, and Hugo died in agonies of remorse and arsenic, with a wild "Ha! ha!"

"I don't see how you can write and act such splendid things, Jo. You're a regular Shakespeare!" exclaimed Beth, who firmly believed that her sisters were gifted with wonderful genius in all things.

"Not quite," replied Jo modestly. "I do think *The Witches' Curse, an Operatic Tragedy*, is rather a nice thing; but I'd like to try *Macbeth*, if we only had a trap-door for Banquo. I always wanted to do the killing part. 'Is this a dagger I see before me?'" muttered Jo, rolling her eyes, and clutching at the air, as she had seen a famous tragedian do.

"No, 'tis the toasting fork, with mother's shoe on it instead of bread."

"Beth's stage-struck!" cried Meg, and the rehearsal ended in a general burst of laughter.

From "Little Women."

"IS THIS A DAGGER I SEE BEFORE ME?"

"HOW THEY BROUGHT THE GOOD NEWS FROM GHENT TO AIX"

By Robert Browning

I sprang to the stirrup, and Joris, and he;
I galloped, Dirck galloped, we galloped all three;
"Good speed!" cried the watch, as the gate-bolts undrew;
"Speed!" echoed the wall to us galloping through;
Behind shut the postern, the lights sank to rest,
And into the midnight we galloped abreast.

Not a word to each other; we kept the great pace
Neck by neck, stride by stride, never changing our place;
I turned in my saddle and made its girths tight,
Then shortened each stirrup, and set the pique right,
Rebuckled the cheek-strap, chained slacker the bit,
Nor galloped less steadily Roland a whit.

'Twas moonset at starting; but while we drew near
Lokeren, the cocks crew and twilight dawned clear;
At Boom, a great yellow star came out to see;
At Düffeld, 'twas morning as plain as could be;
And from Mecheln church-steeple we heard the half-chime,
So Joris broke silence with, "Yet there is time!"

At Aershot, up leaped of a sudden the sun,
And against him the cattle stood black every one,

To stare through the mist at us galloping past,
And I saw my stout galloper Roland at last,
With resolute shoulders, each butting away
The haze, as some bluff river headland its spray:

And his low head and crest, just one sharp ear bent back
For my voice, and the other pricked out on his track;
And one eye's black intelligence, — ever that glance
O'er its white edge at me, his own master, askance!
And the thick, heavy spume-flakes, which aye and anon
His fierce lips shook upwards in galloping on.

By Hasselt, Dirck groaned; and cried Joris, "Stay spur!
Your Roos galloped bravely, the fault's not in her,
We'll remember at Aix" — for one heard the quick wheeze
Of her chest, saw the stretched neck and staggering knees,
And sunk tail, and horrible heave of the flank,
As down on her haunches she shuddered and sank.

So, we were left galloping, Joris and I,
Past Looz and past Tongres, no cloud in the sky;
The broad sun above laughed a pitiless laugh,
'Neath our feet broke the brittle bright stubble like chaff;
Till over by Dalhem a dome-spire sprang white,
And "Gallop," gasped Joris, "for Aix is in sight!"

"How they'll greet us!" — and all in a moment his roan
Rolled neck and croup over, lay dead as a stone;

And there was my Roland to bear the whole weight
Of the news which alone could save Aix from her fate,
With his nostrils like pits full of blood to the brim,
And with circles of red for his eye-sockets' rim.

Then I cast loose my buff coat, each holster let fall,
Shook off both my jack-boots, let go belt and all,
Stood up in the stirrup, leaned, patted his ear,
Called my Roland his pet-name, my horse without peer;
Clapped my hands, laughed and sang, any noise, bad or
        good,
Till at length into Aix Roland galloped and stood.

And all I remember is — friends flocking round
As I sat with his head 'twixt my knees on the ground;
And no voice but was praising this Roland of mine,
As I poured down his throat our last measure of wine,
Which (the burgesses voted by common consent)
Was no more than his due who brought good news from
        Ghent.

Such a starved bank of moss
    Till, that May-morn,
Blue ran the flash across:
    Violets were born!
From "Two Poets of Croisic."   Robert Browning.

LITTLE NELL

By Charles Dickens

Nelly Trent, who has been living in London in poverty with her grandfather, the owner of a curiosity shop, is obliged to flee with him to escape their enemy, Quilp, a cruel and ugly dwarf. With only a small bundle and very little money they make their way out into the open country, walking except when some kindly farmer gives them a lift. Finally they arrive at a churchyard.

The sun was setting when they reached the wicket-gate at which the path began, and as the rain falls upon the just and unjust alike, it shed its warm tint even upon the resting-places of the dead, and bade them be of good hope for its rising on the morrow. The church was old and gray, with ivy clinging to the walls and round the porch.

The old man and the child quitted the gravel path, and strayed among the tombs, for there the ground was soft and easy to their tired feet. As they passed behind the church they heard voices near at hand, and presently came on those who had spoken.

They were two men who were seated in easy attitudes upon the grass, and so busily engaged as to be at first unconscious of intruders. It was not difficult to divine that they were of a class of itinerant showmen—exhibitors of the freaks of Punch, for perched cross-legged upon a tombstone behind them was a figure of that hero himself, his nose and chin as hooked and his face as beaming as usual.

In part scattered upon the ground at the feet of the two men, and in part jumbled together in a long flat box, were the other persons of the drama. Their owners had evidently come to that spot to make some needful repairs in the stage arrangements, for one of them was engaged in binding together a small gallows with thread, while the other was intent upon fixing a new black wig, with the aid of a small hammer and some tacks, upon a head that had been beaten bald.

They raised their eyes when the old man and his young companion were close upon them, and pausing in their work, returned their looks of curiosity. One of them, the actual exhibitor no doubt, was a little merry-faced man with a twinkling eye and a red nose, who seemed to have unconsciously imbibed something of his hero's character. The other—that was he who took the money—had rather a careful and cautious look, which was perhaps inseparable from his occupation also.

The merry man was the first to greet the strangers with a nod; and following the old man's eyes, he observed that perhaps this was the first time he had ever seen a Punch off the stage.

"Why do you come here to do this?" said the old man, sitting down beside them, and looking at the figures with extreme delight.

"Why, you see," answered the little man, "we're putting up for to-night at the public house yonder, and it

wouldn't do to let 'em see the present company undergoing repair."

"No!" cried the old man, making signs to Nell to listen; "why not, eh? why not?"

"Because it would take away all the interest, wouldn't it?" replied the little man. "Would you care a ha'penny for the Lord Chancellor if you know'd him in private and without his wig?—certainly not."

Turning over the figures in the box like one who knew and despised them, Mr. Codlin, the cautious man, drew one forth, and held it up for the inspection of his friend.

"Look here; here's all this Judy's clothes falling to pieces again. You haven't got a needle and thread, I suppose?"

The little man shook his head, and scratched it ruefully. Seeing that they were at a loss, the child said timidly, "I have a needle, sir, in my basket, and thread, too. Will you let me try to mend it for you? I think I could do it neater than you could."

Even Mr. Codlin had nothing to urge against a proposal so seasonable. Nelly, kneeling down beside the box, was soon busy at her task.

While she was thus engaged, the merry little man looked at her with an interest which did not appear to be diminished when he glanced at her helpless companion. When she had finished her work he thanked her, and inquired whither they were traveling.

"N—no farther to-night, I think," said the child, looking towards her grandfather.

"If you're wanting a place to stop at," the man remarked, "I should advise you to take up at the same

house with us. That's it. The long, low, white house
there. It's very cheap."

They all rose and walked away together, Nelly having
hold of her grandfather's hand.

The public house was kept by a fat old landlord and
landlady, who made no objection to receiving their new
guests, and praised Nelly's beauty.

"These two gentlemen have ordered supper in an hour's
time," she said, "and your best plan will be to sup with
them."

When they had been thus received, the whole house
hurried away into an empty stable where the show stood,
and where, by the light of a few flaring candles stuck
round a hoop which hung by a line from the ceiling, it
was to be forthwith exhibited.

And now Mr. Thomas Codlin, the misanthrope, after
blowing away at the Pan's pipes until he was very wretched,
took his station on one side of the checked drapery which
concealed the mover of the figures. Putting his hands in
his pockets he prepared to reply to all questions and re-
marks of Punch, and to make a dismal feint of being his
most intimate, private friend. All this Mr. Codlin did
with his eye slowly wandering about to observe the effect
upon the landlord and landlady, which might lead to very
important results in connection with the supper.

The whole performance was applauded to the echo.
Among the laughter none was more loud and frequent

than the old man's. Nell's was unheard, for she, poor child, with her head drooping on his shoulder, had fallen asleep, and slept too soundly to be roused by any of his efforts to awaken her.

The supper was very good, but she was too tired to eat, and yet would not leave the old man until she had kissed him in his bed.

It was but a loft partitioned into two compartments where they were to rest, but they were well pleased with their lodging, and had hoped for none so good. The old man was uneasy when he had lain down, and begged that Nell would come and sit at his bedside as she had done for so many nights. She hastened to him, and sat there till he slept.

There was a little window, hardly more than a chink in the wall, in her room, and when she left him she opened it, quite wondering at the silence. She had a little money, but it was very little, and when that was gone, they must begin to beg. There was one piece of gold among it, and an emergency might come when its worth to them would be increased a hundredfold. It would be best to hide this coin, and never produce it unless their case was absolutely desperate, and no other resource was left them. Her resolution taken, she sewed the piece of gold into her dress, and going to bed with a lighter heart, sank into a deep slumber.

From "The Old Curiosity Shop." Adapted.

THE STAR SPANGLED BANNER

By Francis Scott Key

This national song was written in September, 1814, while the guns of the British were firing on Fort McHenry, near Baltimore. Key was a prisoner on board a ship of the British fleet and all night long watched the bombardment anxiously. Next morning he wrote this song, which was printed at once and sung to a well-known melody, all over the country.

O say, can you see, by the dawn's early light,
  What so proudly we hailed at the twilight's last gleam-
    ing?
Whose broad stripes and bright stars through the perilous
  fight,
  O'er the ramparts we watched, were so gallantly
    streaming;
And the rockets' red glare, the bombs bursting in air,
Gave proof through the night that our flag was still there:
O say, does that Star Spangled Banner yet wave
O'er the land of the free and the home of the brave?

On that shore, dimly seen through the mists of the deep,
  Where the foe's haughty host in dread silence reposes,
What is that which the breeze, o'er the towering steep,
  As it fitfully blows, now conceals, now discloses?
Now it catches the gleam of the morning's first beam,
In full glory reflected now shines on the stream:

'Tis the Star Spangled Banner; O long may it wave
O'er the land of the free and the home of the brave!

And where is that band who so vauntingly swore
  That the havoc of war and the battle's confusion
A home and a country shall leave us no more—
  Their blood has wash'd out their foul footsteps' pollu-
    tion.
No refuge could save the hireling and slave
From the terror of death, or the gloom of the grave,
And the Star Spangled Banner in triumph shall wave
O'er the land of the free, and the home of the brave!

O thus be it ever, when freemen shall stand
  Between their loved homes and the war's desolation;
Blest with victory and peace, may the heav'n-rescued land
  Praise the Power that hath made and preserved us a
    nation!
Then conquer we must, when our cause it is just,
And this be our motto, "In God is our trust;"
And the Star Spangled Banner in triumph shall wave
O'er the land of the free and the home of the brave!

Let all the ends thou aim'st at be thy country's,
Thy God's and truth's.

From "King Henry VIII." William Shakespeare.

THE COCK AND THE FOX

RETOLD FROM GEOFFREY CHAUCER

Chaucer was an early English poet. In his *Canterbury Tales* he represents a company of pilgrims on their way to the shrine of Thomas à Becket as stopping at the Tabard Inn in Southwark and telling stories as they tarry. The story below is the one told by the "nun priest."

A poor widow, well on in years, once lived in a tiny cottage beside a wood, in a little valley. She had had a very toilsome life ever since she became a widow, for her stock of cattle and her money were both scanty. But she bore her lot simply and patiently, and kept herself and her two daughters by hard work and thrift. She had three large swine, three cows, and a sheep called Moll. Her cottage was a smoky little cabin, just big enough for her wants, and many a frugal meal had the poor woman eaten in it with only hunger for her sauce.

Outside this little house lay a yard with a wooden fence and a dry ditch round it. Here dwelt her cock, Chanticleer by name. In all the land of crowing, there was not his equal to be found. His voice was as sweet as a church organ, and the time of his crowing was surer than any clock. He had a comb redder than fine coral, notched like the battlements of a castle wall. His bill was black, shining like jet, his legs and toes were azure blue; his nails were whiter than the lily-flower, his plumage like burnished gold.

7—4th

Under his rule Chanticleer had seven fair hens, all wondrously like him in color and beauty. But the fairest hues of all were those on the throat of her who was called Dame Partlet, a courteous, discreet and graceful lady, who from the first week of her life had won and kept the heart of her lord Chanticleer. I vow it was a great joy when the sun began to rise to hear them sing together so sweetly their song, "My dear love is far away" (for in those days, as I am told, beasts and birds could speak and sing as men do).

It chanced that one dawn, as Chanticleer sat dozing on his perch, with Dame Partlet by his side, he began to groan in his throat like a man troubled with bad dreams. When Partlet heard the sound, she was afraid, and said: "Dear heart, what ails you that you groan thus? You are a bad sleeper! Fie, for shame!"

"Madam," replied Chanticleer, "I pray you do not take it amiss. My heart is still alarmed from the terror I felt in my sleep. May my dream turn out aright, and no harm come to me! This is what I dreamed: I thought that as I roamed up and down in our yard I saw a beast like a hound, who tried to seize and slay me. His color was between yellow and red, his tail and his ears were tipped with black; his nose was small, and his eyes glowed like fire. I die of fear even now at the thought of his look. That is the cause of my groaning, I do not doubt."

"Fie on you, coward!" quoth Partlet. "Now you have

lost my heart and love. I can not love a coward. I want a husband who is wise and brave, not a boaster who is dazed with fear at any trifle! Why should you be afraid because of a dream? Doubtless it comes from your ill-health. You have eaten food which is not good for you. I pray you, before you eat the herbs which I shall search out from among those that grow in our yard, swallow a worm or so, to make your digestion fit for the plants that will restore you to health. Do not fear your dreams. That is all I have to say to you."

"Wife," answered Chanticleer, "I thank you for your learning and counsel. Now let us talk of something mirthful, and lay aside all these fears. When I see the beauty of your face, dear Partlet, and look on your scarlet eyes, all my dread is driven away. By your side I am so full of joy and hope that I can defy my dreams."

With that he flew down from the perch with all his hens, for it was by now broad day, and with a "Cluck, cluck!" called them to him, having suddenly found a grain of corn lying in the yard. He was no longer afraid, but looked as bold and grim as a lion, roaming proudly up and down on the tips of his toes, and not deigning to set the sole of his foot on the ground at all. Whenever he found any corn he clucked loudly, and out ran all his faithful hens.

A little after, it being then past the month of March, Chanticleer was stalking about in a very grand manner, casting his eyes up to the bright sun, and holding high converse with his seven hens, who were strutting by his side.

"The sun has climbed up in heaven forty-one degrees and more, Dame Partlet," said he. "Hear how the happy birds sing, and see the fresh flowers blowing! My heart is full of mirth and high spirits."

But his joy was destined to end in woe, for suddenly a terrible thing came to pass. A fox, full of treachery and wickedness, who had lived in the wood near the cottage for three years past, had the night before broken through the hedge into the yard where Chanticleer and his hens dwelt. He had been lying quietly in a patch of herbs till it was well advanced in the morning, waiting for his chance to fall upon the cock. Shame upon you, false murderer, lurking in your den! Ah! Chanticleer, woe upon that morning when you flew so proudly down from your perch! You should have taken warning from your dreams.

Fair Partlet lay in the yard with her sisters, bathing herself in the bright sun, and Chanticleer, near by, was singing as merrily as a mermaid. Suddenly, as he cast his eyes upon a butterfly among the herbs, he spied the fox lying there, and his dream came back into his mind with a rush. Not much desire had he then for crowing and singing. He started back aghast, and all he could do was to cry, "Cok, cok!" like one sore afraid. He was about to flee, when the fox spoke and stopped him.

"Gentle sir, alas! why should you go? Are you afraid of me? I am your friend, and I should be base indeed if I wished you any harm. I did not come to spy upon you, but truly I am here only to hear you sing, for your voice is like an angel's. My lord your father (bless his soul!) and your mother, of their grace gave me once the great joy of paying a visit to my house, and I would gladly do you, too, some service.

"I have been told much of what people say about good singing, but I vow that I never heard any man except you sing as well as your father did every morning. What he sang came right from his heart. He would so strain himself to make his voice stronger and clearer that his eyes winked with the loudness of his song, as he stood on tiptoe stretching out his long slender neck. And he was withal so discreet a man that we shall never again find his equal in wisdom.

"I have read in stories of a very famous cock who was clever enough to punish a man who had injured him, but he could not be compared with your father. Now, sir, sing, I pray you, and let me judge if you are really as good as your sire."

Chanticleer was so pleased with this flattery that he did not see what treachery lay hid in it. He flapped his wings, stood up on his tiptoe, stretched out his neck, shut his eyes tight, and crowed lustily. But as soon as he had begun, and was intent on his song, Master Russell the fox started up and caught him by the throat, threw him over his shoulder, and ran off with him toward the woods.

You never heard such lamentation as was raised by Chanticleer's hens when they saw their lord carried off. The widow and her two daughters heard the clamor, and ran out from the cottage, just in time to see the fox bearing the cock away to the woods. They hurried after him, and all the neighbors rushed out with sticks and stones to join in the chase. Forth came Colle the dog, and his friends Talbot and Garland, and Malkin the maid, with her distaff still in her hand. The cow ran, the calf ran, and even the very hogs, roused by the barking of the dogs, the shouting of the men and women, and the din of trumpets and horns and drums, trotted about squealing as if their hearts would break. The ducks quacked, the geese in terror flew away over the tree-tops, the swarm of bees came buzzing out of their hive.

But see now how Fortune sometimes overthrows the hope and pride of victorious conquerors. The cock, lying helpless with fear on the fox's back, suddenly bethought himself of a plan. He began to speak to Master Russell.

"Sir, if I were you I should turn and mock at those who are chasing us, and say, 'Go back, you proud rascals, and not think to catch me. Look, here I am at the woodside, and now the cock will stay with me in spite of all you can do, plague take you! and I will surely eat him very soon.'"

With such words the cock worked on the fox's vanity,
and at last succeeded in his wish.

"Faith, I will do it," said the fox.

With that he made as if to call out to the pursuers. But
no sooner had he opened his mouth to do so than in a

trice the cock had broken away from him, and was perched up in a tree safely out of his reach.

Master Russell saw that he had lost his prey, and fell to his old tricks again. "Alas, Chanticleer!" he said; "I should not have made you afraid of me at first, when I took you from your yard. I vow I did it with no wicked purpose. Come down, and I will tell you the whole truth about what I really meant to do, I promise you."

"No, no, Sir Fox," answered Chanticleer, more wary after his escape. "You do not deceive me twice. You shall not flatter me into shutting my eyes and singing again. A man who shuts his eyes when he ought to be looking about him deserves to have his sight taken away from him."

Thus Chanticleer's dream came true and you can learn from it what it is to be careless and easily flattered. This is the moral of my story: "Take the ripe grain, and let the chaff go." Now may Heaven make us all good men, and bring us to happiness.

From "Tales of the Canterbury Pilgrims." Adapted.

THE DIVERTING HISTORY OF JOHN GILPIN

SHOWING HOW HE WENT FARTHER THAN HE INTENDED, AND CAME
SAFE HOME AGAIN

By WILLIAM COWPER

John Gilpin was a citizen
　　Of credit and renown,
A train-band captain eke was he
　　Of famous London town.

John Gilpin's spouse said to her dear,
　　"Though wedded we have been
These twice ten tedious years, yet we
　　No holiday have seen.

"To-morrow is our wedding-day,
　　And we will then repair
Unto the Bell at Edmonton,
　　All in a chaise and pair.

"My sister, and my sister's child,
　　Myself and children three,
Will fill the chaise, so you must ride
　　On horseback after we."

He soon replied,—"I do admire
　　Of womankind but one,

And you are she, my dearest dear,
    Therefore it shall be done.

"I am a linen-draper bold,
    As all the world doth know,
And my good friend the calender
    Will lend his horse to go."

Quoth Mrs. Gilpin,—"That's well said;
    And for that wine is dear,
We will be furnished with our own,
    Which is both bright and clear."

John Gilpin kissed his loving wife;
    O'erjoyed was he to find,
That, though on pleasure she was bent,
    She had a frugal mind.

The morning came, the chaise was brought,
    But yet was not allowed
To drive up to the door, lest all
    Should say that she was proud.

So three doors off the chaise was stayed,
    Where they did all get in;
Six precious souls, and all agog
    To dash through thick and thin.

Smack went the whip, round went the wheels,
    Were never folk so glad,
The stones did rattle underneath,
    As if Cheapside were mad.

John Gilpin at his horse's side
    Seized fast the flowing mane,
And up he got, in haste to ride,
    But soon came down again;

For saddletree scarce reached had he,
    His journey to begin,
When, turning round his head, he saw
    Three customers come in.

'Twas long before the customers
    Were suited to their mind,
When Betty screaming came down-stairs,
    "The wine is left behind!"

"Good lack!" quoth he, "yet bring it me,
    My leathern belt likewise,
In which I bear my trusty sword
    When I do exercise."

Now Mistress Gilpin (careful soul!)
    Had two stone bottles found,
To hold the liquor that she loved,
    And keep it safe and sound.

Each bottle had a curling ear,
    Through which the belt he drew,
And hung a bottle on each side
    To make his balance true.

Then over all, that he might be
    Equipped from top to toe,
His long red cloak, well brushed and neat,
    He manfully did throw.

Now see him mounted once again
    Upon his nimble steed,
Full slowly pacing o'er the stones,
    With caution and good heed.

But finding soon a smoother road
    Beneath his well-shod feet,
The snorting beast began to trot,
    Which galled him in his seat.

So "Fair and softly," John he cried,
    But John he cried in vain;
That trot became a gallop soon,
    In spite of curb and rein.

Away went Gilpin, neck or nought;
    Away went hat and wig;
He little dreamt, when he set out,
    Of running such a rig.

The dogs did bark, the children screamed,
　Up flew the windows all;
And every soul cried out, " Well done!"
　As loud as he could bawl.

Away went Gilpin—who but he?
　His fame soon spread around;
"He carries weight!"　"He rides a race!"
　" 'Tis for a thousand pound!"

And still as fast as he drew near,
　'Twas wonderful to view,
How in a trice the turnpike men
　Their gates wide open threw.

And now, as he went bowing down
　His reeking head full low,
The bottles twain behind his back
　Were shattered at a blow.

At Edmonton, his loving wife
　From the balcony spied
Her tender husband, wondering much
　To see how he did ride.

"Stop, stop, John Gilpin!—Here's the house!"
　They all at once did cry;
"The dinner waits, and we are tired:"—
　Said Gilpin—"So am I!"

But yet his horse was not a whit
    Inclined to tarry there;
For why?—his owner had a house
    Full ten miles off, at Ware.

So like an arrow swift he flew
    Shot by an archer strong;
So did he fly—which brings me to
    The middle of my song.

Away went Gilpin, out of breath,
    And sore against his will,
Till, at his friend the calender's,
    His horse at last stood still.

The calender, amazed to see
    His neighbor in such trim,
Laid down his pipe, flew to the gate,
    And thus accosted him:

"What news? what news? your tidings tell;
    Tell me you must and shall—
Say why bareheaded you are come,
    Or why you come at all?"

Now Gilpin had a pleasant wit,
    And loved a timely joke;
And thus unto the calender,
    In merry guise, he spoke:

"I came because your horse would come;
    And, if I well forebode,
My hat and wig will soon be here,—
    They are upon the road."

The calender, right glad to find
    His friend in merry pin,
Returned him not a single word,
    But to the house went in;

Whence straight he came with hat and wig;
    A wig that flowed behind,
A hat not much the worse for wear,
    Each comely in its kind.

He held them up, and in his turn,
    Thus showed his ready wit:—
"My head is twice as big as yours,
    They therefore needs must fit.

"But let me scrape the dirt away
    That hangs upon your face;
And stop and eat, for well you may
    Be in a hungry case."

Said John,—"It is my wedding-day,
    And all the world would stare,
If wife should dine at Edmonton,
    And I should dine at Ware."

So turning to his horse, he said,
 "I am in haste to dine;
'Twas for your pleasure you came here,
 You shall go back for mine."

Ah! luckless speech, and bootless boast,
 For which he paid full dear;
For while he spake, a braying ass
 Did sing most loud and clear;

Whereat his horse did snort, as he
 Had heard a lion roar,
And galloped off with all his might,
 As he had done before.

Away went Gilpin, and away
 Went Gilpin's hat and wig;
He lost them sooner than at first,
 For why?—they were too big.

Now Mistress Gilpin, when she saw
 Her husband posting down
Into the country far away,
 She pulled out half-a-crown;

And thus unto the youth she said,
 That drove them to the Bell:
"This shall be yours, when you bring back
 My husband safe and well."

AWAY WENT GILPIN, THE POSTBOY AT HIS HEELS

8—4th

Away went Gilpin, and away
    Went postboy at his heels,
The postboy's horse right glad to miss
    The lumbering of the wheels.

And now the turnpike-gates again
    Flew open in short space;
The toll-men thinking as before,
    That Gilpin rode a race.

And so he did, and won it too,
    For he got first to town;
Nor stopped till where he had got up
    He did again get down.

Now let us sing, Long live the king,
    And Gilpin, long live he;
And when he next doth ride abroad,
    May I be there to see!

Abridged.

ICARUS AND DÆDALUS

A Greek Myth

Among all those mortals who grew so wise that they
ed the secrets of the gods, none was more cunning
Dædalus.

once built, for King Minos of Crete, a wonderful
rinth of winding ways so cunningly tangled up and
twisted around that, once inside, you could never find your
way out again without a magic clue. But the king's favor
veered with the wind, and one day he had his master arch-
itect imprisoned in a tower. Dædalus managed to escape
from his cell; but it seemed impossible to leave the island,
since every ship that came or went was well guarded by
order of the king.

At length, watching the sea-gulls in the air—the only
creatures that were sure of liberty—he thought of a plan
for himself and his young son Icarus, who was captive
with him.

Little by little, he gathered a store of feathers great and
small. He fastened these together with thread, molded
them in with wax, and so fashioned two great wings like
those of a bird. When they were done, Dædalus fitted
them to his own shoulders, and after one or two efforts, he

found that by waving his arms he could winnow the air and cleave it, as a swimmer does the sea. He held himself aloft, wavered this way and that, with the wind, and at last, like a great fledgling, he learned to fly.

Without delay, he fell to work on a pair of wings for the boy Icarus, and taught him carefully how to use them, bidding him beware of rash adventures among the stars. "Remember," said the father, "never to fly very low or very high, for the fogs about the earth would weigh you down, but the blaze of the sun will surely melt your feathers apart if you go too near."

For Icarus, these cautions went in at one ear and out by the other. Who could remember to be careful when he was to fly for the first time? Are birds careful? Not they! And not an idea remained in the boy's head but the one joy of escape.

The day came, and the fair wind that was to set them free. The father put on his wings, and, while the light urged them to be gone, he waited to see that all was well with Icarus, for the two could not fly hand in hand. Up they rose, the boy after his father. The hateful ground of Crete sank beneath them; and the country folk, who caught a glimpse of them when they were high above the tree-tops, took it for a vision of the gods—Apollo, perhaps, with Cupid after him.

At first there was a terror in the joy. The wide vacancy of the air dazed them—a glance downward made their brains reel. But when a great wind filled their wings, and Icarus felt himself sustained, like a halcyon-bird in the hollow of a wave, like a child uplifted by his mother, he forgot everything in the world but joy. He forgot Crete and the other islands that he had passed over: he saw but vaguely the winged thing in the distance before him that was his father Dædalus. He longed for one draft of flight to quench the thirst of his captivity; he stretched out his arms to the sky and made towards the highest heavens.

Alas for him! Warmer and warmer grew the air. Those arms, that had seemed to uphold him, relaxed. His wings wavered, drooped. He fluttered his young hands vainly—he was falling—and in that terror he remembered. The heat of the sun had melted the wax from his wings; the feathers were falling, one by one, like snow-flakes; and there was none to help.

He fell like a leaf tossed down the wind, down, down, with one cry that overtook Dædalus far away. When he returned, and sought high and low for the poor boy, he saw nothing but the bird-like feathers afloat on the water, and he knew that Icarus was drowned.

The nearest island he named Icaria, in memory of the child; but he, in heavy grief, went to the temple of Apollo in Sicily, and there hung up his wings as an offering. Never again did he attempt to fly.

From "Old Greek Folk-Stories," by Josephine Preston Peabody.

DARIUS GREEN AND HIS FLYING-MACHINE

By John Townsend Trowbridge

If ever there lived a Yankee lad,
Wise or otherwise, good or bad,
Who, seeing the birds fly, didn't jump
With flapping arms from stake or stump,
    Or, spreading the tail
    Of his coat for a sail,
Take a soaring leap from post or rail,
    And wonder why
    He couldn't fly,
And flap and flutter and wish and try,—
If ever you knew a country dunce
Who didn't try that as often as once,
All I can say is, that's a sign
He never would do for a hero of mine.

An aspiring genius was D. Green:
The son of a farmer,—age fourteen;
His body was long and lank and lean,—
Just right for flying, as will be seen;
He had two eyes, each bright as a bean,
And a freckled nose that grew between,
A little awry,—for I must mention
That he had riveted his attention

Upon his wonderful invention,
Twisting his tongue as he twisted the strings,
Working his face as he worked the wings,
And with every turn of gimlet and screw
Turning and screwing his mouth round, too,
    Till his nose seemed bent
    To catch the scent,
Around some corner, of new-baked pies,
And his wrinkled cheeks and his squinting eyes
Grew puckered into a queer grimace,
That made him look very droll in the face,
    And also very wise.

And wise he must have been, to do more
Than ever a genius did before,
Excepting Dædalus of yore
And his son Icarus, who wore
    Upon their backs
    Those wings of wax
He had read of in the old almanacs.
Darius was clearly of the opinion,
That the air is also man's dominion,
And that, with paddle or fin or pinion,
    We soon or late
    Shall navigate
The azure as now we sail the sea.
The thing looks simple enough to me;

And if you doubt it,
Hear how Darius reasoned about it.

"Birds can fly,
An' why can't I?
Must we give in,"
Says he with a grin,
"'T the bluebird an' phœbe
Are smarter'n we be?
Jest fold our hands an' see the swaller
An' blackbird an' catbird beat us holler?
Does the leetle, chatterin', sassy wren,
No bigger'n my thumb, know more than men?
Jest show me that!
Er prove't the bat
Has got more brains than's in my hat,
An' I'll back down, an' not till then!"

He argued further: "Ner I can't see
What's th' use o' wings to a bumblebee,
Fer to git a livin' with, more'n to me;—
Ain't my business
Important's his'n is?

"That Icarus
Was a silly cuss,—
Him an' his daddy Dædalus.
They might 'a' knowed wings made o' wax

Wouldn't stan' sun-heat an' hard whacks,
  I'll make mine o' luther,
  Er suthin' er other."

And he said to himself, as he tinkered and planned:
"But I ain't goin' to show my hand
To mummies that never can understand
The fust idee that's big an' grand.
  They'd 'a' laft an' made fun
O' Creation itself afore 't was done!"
So he kept his secret from all the rest,
Safely buttoned within his vest;
And in the loft above the shed
Himself he locks, with thimble and thread
And wax and hammer and buckles and screws,
And all such things as geniuses use;—
Two bats for patterns, curious fellows!
A charcoal-pot and a pair of bellows;
An old hoop-skirt or two, as well as
Some wire and several old umbrellas;
A carriage-cover, for tail and wings;
A piece of harness; and straps and strings;
  And a big strong box,
  In which he locks
These and a hundred other things.

His grinning brothers, Reuben and Burke
And Nathan and Jotham and Solomon, lurk

Around the corner to see him work,—
Sitting cross-leggéd, like a Turk,
Drawing the waxed end through with a jerk,
And boring the holes with a comical quirk
Of his wise old head, and a knowing smirk.
But vainly they mounted each other's backs,
And poked through knot-holes and pried through
   cracks;
With wood from the pile and straw from the stacks
He plugged the knot-holes and calked the cracks;
And a bucket of water, which one would think
He had brought up into the loft to drink
      When he chanced to be dry,
Stood always nigh,
      For Darius was sly!
And whenever at work he happened to spy
At chink or crevice a blinking eye,
He let a dipper of water fly.
"Take that! an' ef ever ye get a peep,
Guess ye'll ketch a weasel asleep!"
      And he sings as he locks
      His big strong box:—

"The weasel's head is small an' trim,
   An' he is leetle an' long an' slim,
      An' quick of motion an' nimble of limb,
         An' ef yeou'll be

Advised by me
Keep wide awake when ye're ketchin' him!"

So day after day
He stitched and tinkered and hammer d away,
Till at last 'twas done,—
The greatest invention under the sun!
"An' now," says Darius, "hooray fer some fun!"

'Twas the Fourth of July,
And the weather was dry,
And not a cloud was on all the sky,
Save a few light fleeces, which here and there,
Half mist, half air,
Like foam on the ocean went floating by:
Just as lovely a morning as ever was seen
For a nice little trip in a flying-machine.

Thought cunning Darius: "Now I shan't go
Along 'ith the fellers to see the show.
I'll say I've got sich a terrible cough!
An' then, when the folks 'ave all gone off,
I'll hev full swing
For to try the thing,
An' practyse a leetle on the wing."

"Ain't goin' to see the celebration?"
Says Brother Nate. "No; botheration!

I've got sich a cold—a toothache—I—
My gracious!—feel's though I should fly!"

    Said Jotham, "Sho!
    Guess ye better go."
    But Darius said, "No!
Shouldn't wonder 'f yeou might see me, though,
'Long 'bout noon, ef I git red
O' this jumpin', thumpin' pain 'n my head."
For all the while to himself he said :—

    "I'll tell ye what!
I'll fly a few times around the lot,
To see how 't seems, then soon's I've got
The hang o' the thing, ez likely's not,
    I'll astonish the nation,
    And all creation,
By flyin' over the celebration!
Over their heads I'll sail like an eagle;
I'll balance myself on my wings like a sea-gull;
I'll dance on the chimbleys; I'll stan' on the steeple;
I'll flop up to winders an' scare the people!
I'll light on the libbe'ty-pole, an' crow;
An' I'll say to the gawpin' fools below,
    'What world's this 'ere
    That I've come near?'
Fer I'll make 'em b'lieve I'm a chap f'm the moon!
An' I'll try a race 'ith their ol' bulloon."

He crept from his bed;
And, seeing the others were gone, he said,
"I'm a gittin' over the cold 'n my head."
And away he sped,
To open the wonderful box in the shed.

His brothers had walked but a little way
When Jotham to Nathan chanced to say,
"What on airth is he up to, hey?"
"Don'o',—the' 's suthin' er other to pay,
Er he wouldn't 'a' stayed to hum to-day."
Says Burke, "His toothache's all 'n his eye!
He never'd miss a Fo'th-o'-July,
Ef he hedn't got some machine to try."

Then Sol, the little one, spoke: "By darn!
Le's hurry back an' hide in the barn,
An' pay him fer tellin' us that yarn!"
"Agreed!"   Through the orchard they creep back,
Along by the fences, behind the stack,
And one by one, through a hole in the wall,
In under the dusty barn they crawl,
Dressed in their Sunday garments all;
And a very astonishing sight was that,
When each in his cobwebbed coat and hat
Came up through the floor like an ancient rat.
And there they hid;
And Reuben slid

The fastenings back, and the door undid.
        "Keep dark!" said he,
"While I squint an' see what the' is to see."

    As knights of old put on their mail,—
            From head to foot
            An iron suit,
    Iron jacket and iron boot,
    Iron breeches, and on the head
    No hat, but an iron pot instead,
            And under the chin the bail,—
    I believe they called the thing a helm;
    And the lid they carried they called a shield;
    And, thus accoutred, they took the field,
    Sallying forth to overwhelm
    The dragons and pagans that plagued the realm:—
            So this modern knight
            Prepared for flight,
    Put on his wings and strapped them tight;
    Jointed and jaunty, strong and light;
    Buckled them fast to shoulder and hip,—
    Ten feet they measured from tip to tip!
    And a helm had he, but that he wore,
    Not on his head like those of yore,
            But more like the helm of a ship.

        "Hush!" Reuben said,
        "He's up in the shed!

He's opened the winder,—I see his head!
  He stretches it out,
  An' pokes it about,
Lookin' to see 'f the coast is clear,
  An' nobody near;—
Guess he don'o' who's hid in here!
He's riggin' a spring-board over the sill!
Stop laffin', Solomon!   Burke, keep still!
He's a climbin' out now—of all the things!
What's he got on?   I van, it's wings!
An' that 'tother thing?   I vum, it's a tail!
An' there he sets like a hawk on a rail!
Steppin' careful, he travels the length
Of his spring-board, and teeters to try its strength.
Now he stretches his wings, like a monstrous bat;
Peeks over his shoulder, this way an' that,
Fer to see 'f the' 's any one passin' by;
But the' 's on'y a ca'f an' a goslin' nigh.
They turn up at him a wonderin' eye,
To see—The dragon! he's goin' to fly!
Away he goes!   Jimminy! what a jump!
  Flop—flop—an' plump
  To the ground with a thump!
Flutt'rin' an' flound'rin', all in a lump!"

As a demon is hurled by an angel's spear,
Heels over head, to his proper sphere,—

Heels over head, and head over heels,
Dizzily down the abyss he wheels,—
So fell Darius. Upon his crown,
In the midst of the barnyard, he came down,
In a wonderful whirl of tangled strings,
Broken braces and broken springs,
Broken tail and broken wings,
Shooting-stars, and various things!
Away with a bellow fled the calf,
And what was that?   Did the gosling laugh?
   'Tis a merry roar
   From the old barn-door,
And he hears the voice of Jotham crying,
"Say, D'rius! how de yeou like flyin'?"
Slowly, ruefully, where he lay,
Darius just turned and looked that way,
As he stanched his sorrowful nose with his cuff.
"Wal, I like flyin' well enough,"
He said; "but the' ain't sich a thunderin' sight
O' fun in 't when ye come to light."

MORAL

I just have room for the moral here:
And this is the moral,—Stick to your sphere.
Or if you insist, as you have the right,
On spreading your wings for a loftier flight,
The moral is,—Take care how you light.

CHRISTMAS AT THE CRATCHITS'

By Charles Dickens

Then up rose Mrs. Cratchit, Cratchit's wife, dressed out but poorly in a twice-turned gown, but brave in ribbons, which are cheap and make a goodly show for sixpence. She laid the cloth, assisted by Belinda Cratchit, second of her daughters, also brave in ribbons; while Master Peter Cratchit plunged a fork into the saucepan of potatoes, and getting the corners of his monstrous shirt-collar (Bob's private property, conferred upon his son and heir in honor of the day) into his mouth, rejoiced to find himself so gallantly attired.

And now two smaller Cratchits, boy and girl, came tearing in screaming that outside the baker's they had smelled the goose, and known it for their own. And basking in luxurious thoughts of sage-and-onion, these young Cratchits danced about the table, and exalted Master Peter Cratchit to the skies, while he (not proud, although his collar nearly choked him) blew the fire until the slow potatoes, bubbling up, knocked loudly at the saucepan lid to be let out and peeled.

"What has ever got your precious father, then?" said Mrs. Cratchit. "And your brother, Tiny Tim? And Martha warn't as late last Christmas Day by half-an-hour!"

"Here's Martha, mother!" said a girl, appearing as she

9—4th

spoke. "Here's Martha, mother!" cried the two young Cratchits. "Hurrah! There's such a goose, Martha!"

"Why, bless your heart alive, my dear, how late you are!" said Mrs. Cratchit, kissing her a dozen times, and taking off her shawl and bonnet for her with officious zeal.

"We'd a deal of work to finish up last night," replied the girl, "and had to clear away this morning, mother!"

"Well! Never mind so long as you are come," said Mrs. Cratchit. "Sit ye down before the fire, my dear, and have a warm, Lord bless ye!"

"No, no! There's father coming," cried the two young Cratchits, who were everywhere at once. "Hide, Martha, hide!"

So Martha hid herself, and in came little Bob, the father, with at least three feet of comforter, exclusive of the fringe, hanging down before him; and his threadbare clothes darned up and brushed, to look seasonable; and Tiny Tim upon his shoulder. Alas for Tiny Tim, he bore a little crutch, and had his limbs supported by an iron frame!

"Why, where's our Martha?" cried Bob Cratchit, looking round.

"Not coming," said Mrs. Cratchit.

"Not coming!" said Bob with a sudden declension in his high spirits, for he had been Tim's blood-horse all the way from church, and had come home rampant. "Not coming upon Christmas Day!"

AND TINY TIM UPON HIS SHOULDER

Martha didn't like to see him disappointed, if it were only in joke; so she came out prematurely from behind the cupboard door, and ran into his arms, while the two young Cratchits hustled Tiny Tim, and bore him off into the wash-house, that he might hear the pudding singing in the copper.

"And how did little Tim behave?" asked Mrs. Cratchit, when she had rallied Bob on his credulity, and Bob had hugged his daughter to his heart's content.

"As good as gold," said Bob, "and better. Somehow he gets thoughtful, sitting by himself so much, and thinks the strangest things you ever heard. He told me, coming home, that he hoped the people saw him in the church, because he was a cripple, and it might be pleasant to them to remember, upon Christmas Day, who made lame beggars walk and blind men see."

Bob's voice was tremulous when he told them this, and trembled more when he said that Tiny Tim was growing strong and hearty.

His active little crutch was heard upon the floor, and back came Tiny Tim before another word was spoken, escorted by his brother and sister to his stool before the fire; and while Bob, turning up his cuffs—as if, poor fellow, they were capable of being made more shabby—compounded some hot mixture in a jug with lemons, and stirred it round and round, and put it on the hob to simmer, Master Peter and the two ubiquitous young Cratchits went to fetch the goose, with which they soon returned in high procession.

Such a bustle ensued that you might have thought a goose the rarest of all birds; a feathered phenomenon, to which a black swan was a matter of course—and in truth it was something very like it in that house. Mrs. Cratchit made the gravy (ready beforehand in a little saucepan) hissing hot; Master Peter mashed the potatoes with incredible vigor; Miss Belinda sweetened up the apple-sauce; Martha dusted the hot plates; Bob took Tiny Tim beside him in a tiny corner at the table; the two young Cratchits set chairs for everybody, not forgetting themselves, and mounting guard upon their posts, crammed spoons into their mouths, lest they should shriek for goose before their turn came to be helped.

At last the dishes were set on, and grace was said. It was succeeded by a breathless pause, as Mrs. Cratchit, looking slowly all along the carving-knife, prepared to plunge it in the breast; but when she did, and when the long expected gush of stuffing issued forth, one murmur of delight arose all round the board, and even Tiny Tim, excited by the two young Cratchits, beat on the table with the handle of his knife, and feebly cried "Hurrah!"

There never was such a goose. Bob said he didn't believe there ever was such a goose cooked. Its tenderness and flavor, size and cheapness, were the themes of universal admiration. Eked out by the apple-sauce and mashed potatoes, it was a sufficient dinner for the whole family; indeed, as Mrs. Cratchit said with great delight (surveying one small atom of a bone upon the dish), "they hadn't eaten it all at last!" Yet every one had had enough, and the youngest Cratchits, in particular, were steeped in sage-and-onion to the eyebrows! But now, the plates being changed by Miss Belinda, Mrs. Cratchit left the room alone—too nervous to bear witness—to take the pudding up and bring it in.

Suppose it should not be done enough! Suppose it should break in turning out! Suppose somebody should have got over the wall of the back yard, and stolen it, while they were merry with the goose—a supposition at which the young Cratchits became livid! All sorts of horrors were supposed.

Hallo! A great deal of steam! The pudding was out of the copper. A smell like a washing-day! That was the cloth. A smell like an eating-house and a pastry-cook's next door to each other, with a laundress' next door to that! That was the pudding! In half a minute Mrs. Cratchit entered—flushed, but smiling proudly—with the pudding, like a speckled cannon-ball, so hard and firm, blazing in ignited brandy, and bedight with Christmas holly stuck into the top.

Oh, a wonderful pudding! Bob Cratchit said, and calmly too, that he regarded it as the greatest success achieved by Mrs. Cratchit since their marriage.

Everybody had something to say about it, but nobody said or thought it was at all a small pudding for a large family. It would have been flat heresy to do so.

At last the dinner was all done, the cloth was cleared, the hearth swept, and the fire made up. The compound in the jug being tasted, and considered perfect, apples and oranges were put upon the table, and a shovelful of chestnuts on the fire. Then all the Cratchit family drew round the hearth in what Bob Cratchit called a circle, meaning half a one; and at Bob Cratchit's elbow stood the family display of glass,—two tumblers, and a custard-cup without a handle.

These held the hot stuff from the jug, however, as well as golden goblets would have done; and Bob served it out with beaming looks, while the chestnuts on the fire sputtered and cracked noisily. Then Bob proposed:

"A Merry Christmas to us all, my dears. God bless us!" Which all the family reëchoed.

"God bless us every one!" said Tiny Tim, the last of all.

From "The Christmas Carol." Abridged.

"God bless us every one!" prayed Tiny Tim,
    Crippled and dwarfed of body, yet so tall
Of soul, we tiptoe earth to look on him,
    High towering over all.

From "God Bless Us Every One." James Whitcomb Riley.

COLUMBUS

By Joaquin Miller

Behind him lay the gray Azores,
    Behind the Gates of Hercules;
Before him not the ghost of shores;
    Before him only shoreless seas.
The good mate said: "Now must we pray,
    For lo! the very stars are gone.
Brave Adm'r'l, speak; what shall I say?"
    "Why, say: 'Sail on! sail on! and on!'"

"My men grow mutinous day by day;
    My men grow ghastly wan and weak."
The stout mate thought of home; a spray
    Of salt wave washed his swarthy cheek.
"What shall I say, brave Adm'r'l, say,
    If we sight naught but seas at dawn?"
"Why, you shall say at break of day:
    'Sail on! sail on! sail on! and on!'"

They sailed and sailed, as winds might blow,
    Until at last the blanched mate said:
"Why, now not even God would know
    Should I and all my men fall dead.
These very winds forget their way,
    For God from these dread seas is gone.

Now speak, brave Adm'r'l; speak and say—"
He said: "Sail on! sail on! and on!"

They sailed.   They sailed.   Then spake the **mate:**
    "This mad sea shows his teeth to-night.
He curls his lip, he lies in wait,
    With lifted teeth, as if to bite!
Brave Adm'r'l, say but one good word:
    What shall we do when hope is gone?"

The words leapt like a leaping sword:
"Sail on! sail on! sail on! and on!"

Then, pale and worn, he kept his deck,
    And peered through darkness.   Ah, that night
Of all dark nights!   And then a speck—
    A light! a light! a light! a light!
It grew, a starlit flag unfurled!
    It grew to be Time's burst of dawn.
He gained a world; he gave that world
    Its grandest lesson: "On! sail on!"

HOW THOR WENT TO THE LAND OF GIANTS

Retold from the Norse Sagas

It was now Thor's turn, and all the company looked eagerly at him, while the king asked by what wonderful feat he chose to distinguish himself.

"I will try a drinking-match with any of you," Thor said shortly; for, to tell the truth, he cared not to perform anything very worthy in the company in which he found himself.

King Utgard appeared pleased with his choice, and when the giants had taken their seats in the hall, he ordered one of his servants to bring in his drinking-cup, which it was his custom to make his guests drain at a draft.

"There!" he said, handing it to Thor, "we call it well drunk if a person empties it at a single draft. Some, indeed, take two to it; but the very weakest can manage it in three."

Thor looked into the cup; it appeared to him deep, but not so very large after all, and, being thirsty, he put it to his lips, and thought to make short work of it, and empty it at one good, hearty pull. He drank, and put the cup down again; but instead of being empty, it was now just so full that it could be moved without spilling.

"Ha! ha! You are keeping all your strength for the second pull, I see," said Utgard, looking in. Without answering, Thor lifted the cup again and drank with all his might till his breath failed; but when he put down the cup, the liquor had only sunk down a little from the brim.

"If you mean to take three drafts to it," said Utgard, "you are really leaving yourself a very unfair share for the last time. Look to yourself, Thor, for if you do not acquit yourself better in other feats, we shall not think so much of you here as they say the gods do in Asgard."

At this speech Thor felt angry, and seizing the cup again, he drank a third time, deeper and longer than he had yet done; but when he looked into the cup, he saw that a very small part only of its contents had disappeared. Wearied and disappointed, he put the cup down, and said he would try no more to empty it.

"It is pretty plain," said the king, looking round on the

company, "that Thor is by no means the kind of man we always supposed him to be."

"Nay," said Thor, "I am willing to try another feat, and you yourselves shall choose what it shall be."

"Well," said the king, "there is a game at which our children are used to play. A short time ago I dared not have named it to Thor; but now I am curious to see how he will bear himself in it. It is merely to lift my cat from the ground—a childish amusement truly."

As he spoke a large gray cat sprang into the hall, and Thor, stooping forward, placed his hand under it to lift it up. He tried gently at first; but by degrees he put forth all his strength, tugging and straining as he had never done before. But the utmost he could do was to raise one of the cat's paws a little way from the ground.

"It's just as I thought," said King Utgard, looking round with a smile; "but we are all willing to allow that the cat is large, and Thor but a little fellow."

"Little as you think me," cried Thor, "who is there who will dare to wrestle with me in my anger?"

"In truth," said the king, "I don't think there is any one here would choose to wrestle with you; but, if wrestle you must, I will call in that old crone, Elli. She has, in her time, laid low many a better man than Thor has shown himself to be."

The crone came. She was old, withered, and toothless, and Thor shrank from the thought of wrestling with her;

but he had no choice. She threw her arms round him, and drew him toward the ground, and the harder he tried to free himself, the tighter grew her grasp. They struggled long.

Thor strove bravely, but a strange feeling of weakness and weariness came over him, and at length he tottered and fell down on one knee before her. At this sight all the giants laughed aloud, and Utgard, coming up, asked the old woman to leave the hall, and said that the trials were over.

No one of his followers would now contend with Thor, he said, and night was approaching. He then invited Thor and his companions to sit down at the table, and spend the night with him as his guests. Thor, though feeling somewhat confused and ashamed, accepted his invitation courteously, and showed, by his agreeable behavior during the evening, that he knew how to bear being conquered with a good grace.

In the morning, when Thor and his companions were leaving the city, the king himself accompanied them without the gates; and Thor, looking steadily at him when he turned to bid him farewell, saw, for the first time, that he was the very same Giant Skrymir with whom he had met in the forest.

"Come now, Thor," said the giant, with a strange sort of smile on his face, "tell me truly, before you go, how you think your journey has turned out, and whether or not I was right in saying that you would meet with better men than yourself in Giants' Home."

"I confess freely," answered Thor, looking up without any false shame on his face, "that I have borne myself but humbly, and it grieves me; for I know that in Giants' Home, henceforward, it will be said I am a man of little worth."

"By my troth! no," cried the giant heartily. "Never should you have come into my city if I had known what a mighty man of valor you really are; and now that you are safely out of it, I will for once tell the truth to you, Thor. All this time I have been deceiving you by my enchantments. When you met me in the forest, and hurled your Mjöllnir at my head, I should have been crushed by the weight of your blows had I not skilfully placed a mountain between myself and you, on which the strokes of your hammer fell, and where you cleft three deep ravines, which shall henceforth become green valleys.

"In the same manner I deceived you about the contests in which you engaged last night. When you took such deep drafts from the horn, you little knew what a wonderful feat you were performing. The other end of that horn reached the ocean, and when you come to the shore you will see how far its waters have fallen away, and how much the deep sea itself has been diminished by your draft. Hereafter, men watching the going out of the tide will call it the ebb, or draft of Thor. Scarcely less wonderful was the bravery you displayed in the second trial. What appeared to you to be a cat, was, in reality, the serpent which encircles the world. When we saw you succeed in moving it, we trembled lest the very foundations of earth and sea should be shaken by your strength.

"Nor need you be ashamed of having been overthrown by the old woman, for she is Old Age; and there never has, and never will be, one whom she has not the power to lay low. We must now part, and you had better not come here again, or attempt anything further against my city; for I shall always defend it by fresh enchantments, and you will never be able to do anything against me."

At these words Thor raised Mjöllnir, and was about to challenge the giant to a fresh trial of strength; but, before he could speak, Skrymir vanished from his sight; and, turning round to look for the city, he found that it, too, had disappeared, and that he was standing alone on a smooth, green, empty plain.

From "The Heroes of Asgard," by A. and E. Keary.   Adapted.

I am the God Thor,
I am the War God,
I am the Thunderer!
Here in my Northland,
My fastness and fortress,
Reign I for ever!

From "The Challenge of Thor."   Henry Wadsworth Longfellow.

HORATIUS AT THE BRIDGE

By Thomas Babington Macaulay

Legend tells that on a day when Rome was threatened with invasion by the Etruscans, Horatius Cocles and two companions volunteered to hold the bridge across the Tiber until the Romans should have time to hew it down and thus prevent the enemy's entrance. Victory for the Etruscans meant for Rome once more the hated government of Tarquinius, who had been driven out. As the bridge tottered, the companions of Horatius rushed back to safety

<blockquote>
Alone stood brave Horatius,
    But constant still in mind;
Thrice thirty thousand foes before,
    And the broad flood behind.
"Down with him!" cried false Sextus,
    With a smile on his pale face.
"Now yield thee," cried Lars Porsena,
    "Now yield thee to our grace."

Round turned he, as not deigning
    Those craven ranks to see;
Naught spake he to Lars Porsena,
    To Sextus naught spake he;
But he saw on Palatinus
    The white porch of his home;
And he spake to the noble river
    That rolls by the towers of Rome,
</blockquote>

"Oh, Tiber! Father Tiber!
    To whom the Romans pray,
A Roman's life, a Roman's arms,
    Take thou in charge this day!"
So he spake, and, speaking, sheathed
    The good sword by his side,
And, with his harness on his back,
Plunged headlong in the tide.

No sound of joy or sorrow
    Was heard from either bank;
But friends and foes in dumb surprise,
With parted lips and straining eyes,
    Stood gazing where he sank;
And when above the surges
    They saw his crest appear,
All Rome sent forth a rapturous cry,
And even the ranks of Tuscany
    Could scarce forbear to cheer.

"Curse on him!" quoth false Sextus;
    "Will not the villain drown?
But for this stay, ere close of day
    We should have sacked the town!"
"Heaven help him!" quoth Lars Porsena,
    "And bring him safe to shore;
For such a gallant feat of arms
    Was never seen before."

And now he feels the bottom;
  Now on dry earth he stands;
Now round him throng the Fathers
  To press his gory hands;
And now, with shouts and clapping,
  And noise of weeping loud,
He enters through the River Gate,
  Borne by the joyous crowd.

They gave him of the corn-land,
  That was of public right,
As much as two strong oxen
  Could plow from morn till night;
And they made a molten image,
  And set it up on high,
And there it stands unto this day
 . To witness if I lie.

It stands in the Comitium,
  Plain for all folk to see;
Horatius in his harness,
  Halting upon one knee:
And underneath is written,
  In letters all of gold,
How valiantly he kept the bridge
  In the brave days of old.

        Abridged.

KING JOHN AND THE ABBOT OF CANTERBURY

An English Folk Tale

In the reign of King John there lived an Abbot of Canterbury who kept up grand state in his Abbey. A hundred of the Abbot's men dined each day with him, and fifty knights in velvet coats and gold chains waited upon him. Well, King John, as you know, was a very bad king, and he couldn't brook the idea of any one in his kingdom, however holy, being honored more than he. So he summoned the Abbot of Canterbury to his presence.

The Abbot came with a goodly retinue, with his fifty knights-at-arms in velvet cloaks and gold chains. The king went to meet him, and said to him: "How now, Father Abbot? I hear it of thee, thou keepest far greater state than I. This becomes not our royal dignity, and savors of treason in thee."

"My liege," quoth the Abbot, bending low, "I beg to say that all I spend has been freely given to the Abbey out of the piety of the folk. I trust your Grace will not take it ill that I spend for the Abbey's sake what is the Abbey's."

"Nay, proud prelate," answered the king, "all that is in this fair realm of England is our own, and thou hast no right to put me to shame by holding such state. However, of my clemency I will spare thee thy life and thy property if thou canst answer me but three questions."

"I will do so, my liege," said the Abbot, "so far as my poor wit can extend."

"Well, then," said the king, "tell me where is the center of all the round world; then let me know how soon can I ride the whole world about; and, lastly, tell me what I think."

"Your Majesty jesteth," stammered the Abbot.

"Thou wilt find it no jest," said the king. "Unless thou canst answer me these questions three before a week is out, thy head will leave thy body," and he turned away.

Well, the Abbot rode off in fear and trembling, and first he went to Oxford to see if any learned doctor could tell him the answer to those questions three; but none could help him, and he went his way to Canterbury, sad and sorrowful, to take leave of his monks. But on the road he met his shepherd as he was going to the fold.

"Welcome home, Lord Abbot," quoth the shepherd; "what news from good King John?"

"Sad news, sad news, my shepherd," said the Abbot, and told him all that had happened.

"Now, cheer up, Sir Abbot," said the shepherd. "A fool may perhaps answer what a wise man knows not. I will go to London in your stead; grant me only your apparel and your retinue of knights. At the least I can die in your place."

"Nay, shepherd, not so," said the Abbot; "I must meet

THE ABBOT CAME WITH A GOODLY RETINUE

the danger in my own person. And as to that, thou canst not pass for me."

"But I can and I will, Sir Abbot. In a cowl, who will know me for what I am?"

So at last the Abbot consented, and sent him to London in his own most splendid array. He approached King John with all the Abbot's retinue, but dressed in his simple monk's dress, and with his cowl over his face.

"Now welcome, Sir Abbot," said King John; "thou art prepared for thy doom, I see."

"I am ready to answer your Majesty," said he.

"Well, then, question first: Where is the center of the round earth?" said the king.

"Here," said the shepherd Abbot, planting his crozier in the ground. "And your Majesty believe me not, go measure it and see."

"A merry answer and a shrewd," said the king; "so to question the second: How soon may I ride this round world about?"

"If your Majesty will graciously rise with the sun, and ride along with him until the next morning he rise, your Grace will surely have ridden it round."

"I did not think it could be done so soon," laughed King John. "But let that pass, and tell me question third and last, and that is: What do I think?"

"That is easy, your Grace," said he. "Your Majesty thinks I am my lord, the Abbot of Canterbury; but as you may see"—and here he raised his cowl—"I am but

his poor shepherd, that am come to ask your pardon
for him and for me."

Loud laughed the king. "Well caught! Thou hast more
wit than thy lord, and thou shalt be Abbot in his place."

"Nay, that can not be," quoth the shepherd; "I know
not how to write nor to read."

"Well, then, four nobles a week thou shalt have for thy
ready wit. And tell the Abbot from me that he has my
pardon." And with that King John sent away the shepherd with a right royal present, besides his pension.

From Joseph Jacobs's "More English Fairy Tales." Adapted.

THE EARTHEN POT AND THE POT OF BRASS

A river having overflowed its banks, two pots, one made
of Earthenware and the
other of Brass, were car-
ried along in the stream.
"Well, brother, since we
share the same fate, let us
go along together," cried
the Brazen Pot to the
Earthen one. "No!" re-
plied the latter in a great
fright; "keep off, what-

ever you do, for if you knock against me, or I against you,
it will be all over with me—to the bottom I shall go."

Æsop.

"I WANDERED LONELY AS A CLOUD"

By WILLIAM WORDSWORTH

Of the three famous poets whose names are linked with the beautiful Lake Country of England—Wordsworth, Coleridge and Southey—Wordsworth's life and work especially belong to it. Most of his poems are about nature, or thoughts inspired by it. He was born, in 1770, at Cockermouth, Cumberland, at one end of this district, and went to school in quaint old Hawkshead at the other end. In its woods he searched for nuts, on its grassy moors he caught woodcock, and he climbed its steep crags in hunting the raven. Here it was— at Grasmere—that he returned, after  his studies at Cambridge University and his travels abroad, to live, and to write. A visit from Coleridge made him determine to be a poet. Nearly all of his poems were composed under the open sky, as he was walking along hill or lake side. A stranger who visited Rydal Mount, as Wordsworth's home was called, asked to see where he worked. The servant took him first into a room filled with books. "This," said she, "is my master's library, but his study is out of doors." On his daily jaunts Wordsworth not only composed poems, but visited the cottagers far and near. When his birthday came they repaid his interest in them by gathering at his home for a merry old English festival. Sometimes with his own hands he planted a holly-tree to make a hillside more beautiful. By those who were closest to him, especially his sister

Dorothy, his wife and his daughter, Wordsworth was revered and greatly loved. "Large-boned, lean but still firm-knit, tall and strong-looking when he stood, a right good old steel-gray figure," Carlyle found him. Hazlitt says that there was "a peculiar sweetness in his smile," and De Quincy, that in his eyes was "a light which seems to come from depths below all depths." Wordsworth succeeded Southey as poet laureate. He died in 1850.

I wandered lonely as a cloud
That floats on high o'er vales and hills,
When all at once I saw a crowd,
A host of golden daffodils;
Beside the lake, beneath the trees,
Fluttering and dancing in the breeze.

Continuous as the stars that shine
And twinkle on the milky way,
They stretched in never-ending line
Along the margin of a bay:
Ten thousand saw I at a glance,
Tossing their heads in sprightly dance.

The waves beside them danced; but they
Out-did the sparkling waves in glee:
A poet could not but be gay
In such a jocund company:
I gazed—and gazed—but little thought
What wealth the show to me had brought:

For oft, when on my couch I lie
In vacant or in pensive mood,
They flash upon that inward eye
Which is the bliss of solitude;
And then my heart with pleasure fills,
And dances with the daffodils.

MAGGIE VISITS THE GIPSIES

By George Eliot

"November 22, 1819, Mary Ann Evans was born at Arbury Farm at five o'clock this morning." Thus speaks the old diary kept by George Eliot's father. From her father, a man of unusual worth, George Eliot, as she became known to the world through her pen-name, inherited many qualities, especially that habit of taking pains, which so surely goes with genius. In the green War-wickshire country in England she lived a happy childhood, having for chief playmate a somewhat older brother whom she adored.

The Mill on the Floss, from which the story below is taken, pictures much of her family life beside the hurrying Floss which in the novel replaces the "brown canal" of her real home scene. After boarding school she went to London, where she helped edit the *Westminster Review*, and became the center of a rare literary circle, including Herbert Spencer. Modest as to her own powers, it was not until she was forty that she published *Adam Bede*, her first novel. While preparing for *Romola*, another of her novels, the scene of which is laid in Florence in the middle ages, she read more than a thousand books. Charles Dickens was the first to guess the new writer to be a woman. George Eliot died in 1880.

Maggie Tulliver, having gone with her brother Tom to visit their aunt, falls out with him. Fancying herself greatly injured she resolves to run away to a Gipsy camp which she knows to be in the neighborhood. After running and walking a long way she finally comes upon the Gipsies gathered around their fire at the foot of a lane.

"My little lady, where are you going?" the Gipsy said, in a coaxing tone.

It was delightful, and just what Maggie expected. The Gipsies saw at once that she was a little lady, and were prepared to treat her accordingly.

"Not any farther," said Maggie, feeling as if she were saying what she had rehearsed in a dream. "I'm coming to stay with you, please."

"That's pretty; come, then. Why, what a nice little lady you are, to be sure!" said the Gipsy, taking her by the hand. Maggie thought her very agreeable, but wished she had not been so dirty.

There was quite a group round the fire when they reached it. An old Gipsy woman was seated on the ground nursing her knees, and poking a skewer into the

round kettle that sent forth an odorous steam. Two
small shock-headed children were lying prone and resting
on their elbows. And a placid donkey was bending his
head over a tall girl, who, lying on her back, was scratch-
ing his nose and indulging him with a bite of excellent
stolen hay.

The slanting sunlight fell kindly upon them, and the
scene was really very pretty and comfortable, Maggie
thought, only she hoped they would soon set out the
tea-cups.

"Oh, what a nice little lady!—and rich, I'm sure,"
said the old woman. "Didn't you live in a beautiful
house at home?"

"Yes, my home is pretty, and I'm very fond of the
river, where we go fishing, but I'm often very unhappy.
I should have liked to bring my books with me, but I
came away in a hurry, you know. But I can tell you
almost everything there is in my books, I've read them
so many times, and that will amuse you. And I can tell
you something about geography, too,—that's about the
world we live in,—very useful and interesting. Did you
ever hear about Columbus?"

Maggie's eyes had begun to sparkle and her cheeks to
flush,—she was really beginning to instruct the Gipsies,
and gaining great influence over them. The Gipsies themselves were not without amazement at this talk, though
their attention was divided by the contents of Maggie's

pocket, which the friend at her right hand had by this time emptied without attracting her notice.

"Is that where you live, my little lady?" said the old woman, at the mention of Columbus.

"Oh, no!" said Maggie, with some pity. "Columbus was a very wonderful man, who found out half the world, and they put chains on him and treated him very badly, you know. It's in my geography, but perhaps it's rather too long to tell before tea—I want my tea so." The last words burst from Maggie, in spite of herself.

"Why, she's hungry, poor little lady," said the younger woman. "Give her some of the cold victual. You've been walking a good way, I'll be bound, my dear. Where's your home?"

"It's Dorlcote Mill, a long way off," said Maggie. "My father is Mr. Tulliver, but we mustn't let him know where I am, or he will take me home again. Where does the queen of the Gipsies live?"

"What! do you want to go to her, my little lady?" said the younger woman. The tall girl, meanwhile, was constantly staring at Maggie and grinning. Her manners were certainly not agreeable.

"No," said Maggie, "I'm only thinking that if she isn't a very good queen you might be glad when she died, and you could choose another. If I were queen, I'd be a very good queen, and kind to everybody."

"Here's a bit of nice victual, then," said the old woman,

handing to Maggie a lump of dry bread, which she had taken from a bag of scraps, and a piece of cold bacon.

"Thank you," said Maggie, looking at the food without taking it; "but will you give me some bread and butter and tea instead? I don't like bacon."

"We've got no tea or butter," said the old woman, with something like a scowl, as if she were getting tired of coaxing.

Then the old woman, seeming to forget Maggie's hunger, poked the skewer into the pot with new vigor, and the younger crept under the tent and reached out some platters and spoons. Maggie trembled a little, and was afraid the tears would come into her eyes.

But the springing tears were checked by new terror, when two men came up. The elder of the two carried a bag, which he flung down, addressing the women in a loud and scolding tone, which they answered by a shower of sauciness. A black dog ran barking up to Maggie, and threw her into a tremor that found only a new cause in the curses with which the younger man called the dog off, and gave him a rap with a great stick he held in his hand.

Maggie felt that it was impossible that she should ever be queen of these people, or even give them amusing and useful knowledge.

Both the men now seemed to be asking about Maggie, for they looked at her. At last the younger woman said, in her coaxing tone, "This nice little lady's come to live with us; aren't you glad?"

"Ay, very glad," said the younger man, who was looking at Maggie's silver thimble and other small matters that had been taken from her pocket. He returned them all, except the thimble, to the younger woman, with some remark, and she put them again in Maggie's pocket. The men seated themselves, and began to attack the contents of the kettle,—a stew of meat and potatoes,—which had been taken off the fire and turned out into a yellow platter.

Maggie began to think that Tom must be right about the Gipsies, they must certainly be thieves, unless the man meant to return her thimble by and by. She would willingly have given it to him, for she was not at all attached to her thimble. But the idea that she was among thieves prevented her from feeling any comfort. The women saw that she was frightened.

"We've nothing nice for a lady to eat," said the old woman, in her coaxing tone. "And she's so hungry, sweet little lady."

"Here, my dear, try if you can eat a bit of this," said the younger woman, handing some of the stew on a brown dish with an iron spoon to Maggie, who remembered that the old woman had seemed angry with her for not liking the bread and bacon, and dared not refuse the stew, though fear had chased away her appetite. If her father would only come by in the gig and take her up!

"What! you don't like the smell of it, my dear," said the young woman, observing that Maggie did not even take a spoonful of the stew. "Try a bit, come."

"No, thank you," said Maggie, trying to smile in a friendly way. "I haven't time, I think; it seems getting darker. I think I must go home now, and come again another day, and then I can bring you a basket with some jam tarts and things."

Maggie rose from her seat; but her hope sank when the old Gipsy woman said, "Stop a bit, stop a bit, little lady; we'll take you home, all safe, when we've done supper; you shall ride home, like a lady."

Maggie sat down again, with little faith in this promise, though she presently saw the tall girl putting a bridle on the donkey, and throwing a couple of bags on his back.

"Now then, little missis," said the younger man, rising, and leading the donkey forward, "tell us where you live; what's the name of the place?"

"Dorlcote Mill is my home," said Maggie eagerly. "My father is Mr. Tulliver; he lives there."

"What! a big mill a little way this side of St. Ogg's?"

"Yes," said Maggie. "Is it far off? I think I should like to walk there, if you please."

"No, no, it'll be getting dark, we must make haste. And the donkey'll carry you as nice as can be; you'll see."

He lifted Maggie as he spoke, and set her on the donkey. She felt relieved that it was not the old man who seemed to be going with her, but she had only a trembling hope that she was really going home.

"Here's your pretty bonnet," said the younger woman, putting it on Maggie's head; "and you'll say we've been very good to you, won't you? and what a nice little lady we said you were."

"Oh, yes, thank you," said Maggie, "I'm very much obliged to you. But I wish you'd go with me, too." She thought anything was better than going with one of the dreadful men alone.

"Ah, you're fondest of me, aren't you?" said the woman. "But I can't go; you'll go too fast for me."

It now appeared that the man also was to be seated on the donkey, holding Maggie before him, and no nightmare had ever seemed more horrible. When the woman had patted her on the back, and said "Good-by," the donkey set off at a rapid walk along the lane toward the point Maggie had come from an hour ago.

No one was ever more terrified than poor Maggie in this ride on a short-paced donkey, with a Gipsy behind her, who considered that he was earning half a crown. The red light of the setting sun seemed to have a dreadful mean- ing, with which the alarming bray of the second donkey with the log on its foot must surely have some connection. Two low-thatched cottages — the only houses they passed in this lane — seemed to add to its dreariness. They had no windows to speak of, and the doors were closed; it was

11—4th

probable that they were inhabited by witches, and it was a relief to find that the donkey did not stop there.

At last—oh, sight of joy!—this lane, the longest in the world, was coming to an end, was opening on a broad highroad, where there was actually a coach passing! And there was a finger-post at the corner—she had surely seen that finger-post before—"To St. Ogg's, 2 miles."

The Gipsy really meant to take her home, then; he was probably a good man, after all, and might have been rather hurt at the thought that she didn't like coming with him alone. This idea became stronger as she felt more and more certain that she knew the road quite well. She was thinking how she might open a conversation with the injured Gipsy, when, as they reached a cross-road, Maggie caught sight of some one coming on a white-faced horse.

"Oh, stop, stop!" she cried out. "There's my father! Oh, father, father!"

The sudden joy was almost painful, and before her father reached her, she was sobbing. Great was Mr. Tulliver's wonder, for he had made a round from Basset, and had not yet been home.

"Why, what's the meaning of this?" he said, checking his horse, while Maggie slipped from the donkey and ran to her father's stirrup.

"The little miss lost herself, I reckon," said the Gipsy. "She'd come to our tent at the far end of Dunlow Lane, and I was bringing her where she said her home was. It's a good way to come after being on the tramp all day."

"Oh, yes, father, he's been very good to bring me home," said Maggie. "A very kind, good man!"

"Here, then, my man," said Mr. Tulliver, taking out five shillings. "It's the best day's work you ever did. I couldn't afford to lose the little lass; here, lift her up before me."

"Why, Maggie, how's this, how's this?" he said, as they rode along, while she laid her head against her father and sobbed. "How came you to be rambling about and lose yourself?"

"Oh, father," sobbed Maggie, "I ran away because I was so unhappy. Tom was so angry with me. I couldn't bear it."

"Pooh, pooh," said Mr. Tulliver soothingly, "you mustn't think of running away from father. What would father do without his little lass?"

"Oh, no, I never will again, father—never."

Mr. Tulliver spoke his mind very strongly when he reached home that evening; and the effect was seen in the fact that Maggie never heard one reproach from her mother or one taunt from Tom about this foolish business of her running away to the Gipsies. Maggie was rather awe-struck by this unusual treatment, and sometimes thought her conduct had been too wicked to be alluded to.

From "The Mill on the Floss."

TO THE FRINGED GENTIAN

By William Cullen Bryant

Thou blossom bright with autumn dew,
And colored with the heaven's own blue,
That openest when the quiet light
Succeeds the keen and frosty night,

Thou comest not when violets lean
O'er wandering brooks and springs unseen,
Or columbines, in purple dressed,
Nod o'er the ground-bird's hidden nest.

Thou waitest late and com'st alone,
When woods are bare and birds are flown,
And frosts and shortening days portend
The aged year is near his end.

Then doth thy sweet and quiet eye
Look through its fringes to the sky,
Blue—blue—as if that sky let fall
A flower from its cerulean wall.

I would that thus, when I shall see
The hour of death draw near to me,
Hope, blossoming within my heart,
May look to Heaven as I depart.

The apple is the commonest and yet the most varied and beautiful of fruits. A dish of them is as becoming to the center-table in winter as was the vase of flowers in the summer—a bouquet of spitzenbergs and greenings and northern spies. A rose when it blooms, the apple is a rose when it ripens. It pleases every sense to which it can be addressed, the touch, the smell, the sight, the taste; and when it falls in the still October day it pleases the ear. It is a call to a banquet; it is a signal that the feast is ready. The bough would fain hold it, but it can now assert its independence; it can now live a life of its own.

From "Winter Sunshine."   *John Burroughs.*

LEARNING BY OBSERVATION

By Charles Kingsley

"A genuine, out-of-doors English boy" wrote one of Charles Kingsley's teachers about him in after years. "We well remember

his description of a hunt after some pigs from which he returned with his head torn with brambles and his face beaming with fun and frolic." He worked hard at his lessons, but sometimes his fancy would run away with him. One day while reciting Latin to his father he kept his eyes fixed on the red coals in the grate. All at once he stopped in the middle of a sentence. "I do declare," he said, "there are pirates in the coal." His father was a minister whose changes from one church to another gave the boy a varied life. From rolling Devonshire County—England's garden spot—he went to the flat fens, and thence at eleven to the sea-coast. Here, with his brother, he delighted in long rambles over the rocky cliffs, searching for rare shells and for strange seaweeds and flowers. He had sharp eyes for anything new and interesting to add to his stores. When, one day, a new housemaid threw away his treasures he was very unhappy. His grandfather had lived in the West Indies, and the stories he told of the life there and of old war times charmed the boy. He was brave to bear pain, was gentle, shy and rather delicate despite his hardy sports with boat and ponies. When the herring-boats put out to sea, Charles's father held parting services at the shore for the fishermen and their families. These farewells deeply impressed him and when he grew up he wrote a poem called *The Three Fishers*, men who must leave home, "Though storms be sudden, and waters deep."

After the years by the sea came London, a public school, and Cambridge University, where young Kingsley's papers showed much talent. Kingsley's life was very active. Always he was writing, lecturing, preaching or working among the poor. Honors came to him and much love. He died not long after a visit to America. His body was buried at Eversley Church where he had served many years. [Born in 1819—died in 1875]

The great use of a school education is not so much to teach you things, as to teach you how to learn,—to give you the noble art of learning, which you can use for yourselves in after life on any matter to which you choose to turn your mind. And what does the art of learning consist in? First and foremost, in the art of observing. That is, the boy who uses his eyes best on his book, and observes the words and letters of his lesson most accurately and carefully, that is the boy who learns his lesson best.

You know as well as I how one boy will sit staring at his book for an hour, without knowing a word about it, while another will learn the thing in a quarter of an hour; and why? Because one has actually not seen the words. He has been thinking of something else, looking out of the window, repeating the words to himself like a parrot. The other has simply, as we say, "looked sharp." He has looked at the lesson with his whole mind, seen it, and seen into it, and therefore knows all about it.

Therefore I say that everything which helps a boy's

powers of observation helps his power of learning; and I know from experience that nothing helps that so much as the study of the world about us, and especially of natural history; to be accustomed to watch for curious objects, to know in a moment when you have come upon anything new,—which is observation; to be quick at seeing when things are like and when unlike,—which is classification. All that must, and I well know does, help to make a boy shrewd, earnest, accurate, ready for whatever may happen.

When we were little and good, a long time ago, we used to have a jolly old book called *Evenings at Home,* in which was a great story, called *Eyes and No Eyes;* and that story was of more use to me than any dozen other stories I ever read.

A regular old-fashioned story it is, but a right good one, and thus it begins—

"Well, Robert, where have you been walking this after- noon?" said Mr. Andrews, to one of his pupils, at the close of a holiday.   Oh, Robert had been to Broom Heath, and round to Campmount, and home through the mead- ows.   But it was very dull; he hardly saw a single person. He would rather by half have gone by the turnpike road.

"But where is William?"

Oh, William started with him, but he was so tedious, always stopping to look at this thing or that, that Robert would rather walk alone, and so went on.

Presently in comes Master William, dressed, no doubt,

as we wretched boys used to be forty years ago,—frill collar, and tight monkey-jacket, and tight trousers buttoned over it, a pair of low shoes which always came off if stepped into heavy ground; and terribly dirty and wet he is, but he never had such a pleasant walk in his life, and he has brought home a handkerchief full of curiosities.

He has got a piece of mistletoe, and wants to know what it is, and has seen a woodpecker and a wheat-ear, and got strange flowers off the heath, and hunted a peewit, because he thought its wing was broken, till of course it led him into a bog, and wet he got; but he did not mind, for in the bog he fell in with an old man cutting turf, who told him all about turf-cutting; and then he went up a hill, and saw a grand prospect, and because the place was called Campmount he looked for a Roman camp, and found the ruins of one; and then he went on and saw twenty things more; and so on, and so on, till he had brought home curiosities enough and thoughts enough to last him a week.

Mr. Andrews, who seems a sensible old gentleman, tells him all about his curiosities; and then it turns out that Master William has been over exactly the same ground as Master Robert, who saw nothing at all.

Whereon, says Mr. Andrews, wisely enough, in his solemn, old-fashioned way: "So it is; one man walks through the world with his eyes open, and another with them shut; and upon this depends all the superiority of knowledge which one acquires over the other. I have known sailors who had been in all quarters of the world, and could tell you nothing but the signs of the tippling-houses, and the price and quality of the liquor. On the other hand, Franklin could not cross the Channel without making observations useful to mankind.

"While many a vacant, thoughtless person is whirled through Europe without gaining a single idea worth crossing the street for, the observing eye and inquiring mind find matter of improvement and delight in every ramble. Do you, then, William, continue to make use of your eyes; and you, Robert, learn that eyes were given you to use."

And when I read that story, as a little boy, I said to myself, I will be Mr. Eyes; I will not be Mr. No Eyes; and Mr. Eyes I have tried to be ever since; and Mr. Eyes I advise you, every one of you, to be, if you wish to be happy and successful.

Ah! boys, if you knew the idle, vacant, useless life which many young men lead when their day's work is done, continually tempted to sin and shame and ruin by their own idleness, while they miss opportunities of making valuable discoveries, of distinguishing themselves and helping themselves forward in life, then you would make it a duty to get a habit of observing, and of having some healthy pursuit with which to fill up your leisure hours.

From " Madam How and Lady Why."

NUREMBERG

BY HENRY WADSWORTH LONGFELLOW

In the valley of the Pegnitz, where across broad meadow-
lands

Rise the blue Franconian mountains, Nuremberg, the ancient, stands.

Quaint old town of toil and traffic, quaint old town of art
and song,

Memories haunt thy pointed gables, like the rooks that
round them throng:

Memories of the Middle Ages, when the emperors, rough
and bold,

Had their dwelling in thy castle, time-defying, centuries
old;

And thy brave and thrifty burghers boasted, in their
　　uncouth rhyme,
That their great imperial city stretched its hand through
　　every clime.

In the court-yard of the castle, bound with many an iron
　　band,
Stands the mighty linden planted by Queen Cunigunde's
　　hand;

Everywhere I see around me rise the wondrous world of
　　Art:
Fountains wrought with richest sculpture standing in the
　　common mart.

In the church of sainted Sebald sleeps enshrined his holy
　　dust,
And in bronze the Twelve Apostles guard from age to age
　　their trust;

In the church of sainted Lawrence stands a pix of
　　sculpture rare,
Like the foamy sheaf of fountains, rising through the
　　painted air.

Here, when Art was still religion, with a simple, reverent
      heart,
Lived and labored Albrecht Dürer, the Evangelist of Art;

Hence in silence and in sorrow, toiling still with busy hand,
Like an emigrant he wandered, seeking for the Better
      Land.

Emigravit is the inscription on the tombstone where he
      lies;
Dead he is not, but departed,—for the artist never dies.

Fairer seems the ancient city, and the sunshine seems
      more fair,
That he once has trod its pavement, that he once has
      breathed its air!

Through these streets so broad and stately, these obscure
    and dismal lanes,
Walked of yore the Mastersingers, chanting rude poetic
    strains.

From remote and sunless suburbs came they to the friendly
    guild,
Building nests in Fame's great temple, as in spouts the
    swallows build.

As the weaver plied the shuttle, wove he too the mystic
    rhyme,
And the smith his iron measures hammered to the anvil's
    chime;

Thanking God, whose boundless wisdom makes the flowers
    of poesy bloom
In the forge's dust and cinders, in the tissues of the loom.

Here Hans Sachs, the cobbler-poet, laureate of the gentle
    craft,
Wisest of the Twelve Wise Masters, in huge folios sang
    and laughed.

Vanished is the ancient splendor, and before my dreamy
    eye
Wave these mingled shapes and figures, like a faded
    tapestry.

*The Statue
of Hans Sachs
at Nuremberg*

Not thy Councils, not thy Kaisers, win for thee the
    world's regard;
But thy painter, Albrecht Dürer, and Hans Sachs, thy
    cobbler bard.

Thus, O Nuremberg, a wanderer from a region far away,
As he paced thy streets and court-yards, sang in thought
    his careless lay:

Gathering from the pavement's crevice, as a floweret of
    the soil,
The nobility of labor,—the long pedigree of toil.

Abridged.

COSETTE

By Victor Hugo

Cosette drew out the bucket of water nearly full and set it on the grass. The forest was dark. A cold wind was blowing. She seized the handle of the bucket with both hands and advanced a dozen paces. But she was forced to set it on the ground once more. After some seconds of repose she set out again. The weight of the bucket strained and stiffened her thin arms. Each time she halted, cold water splashed on her bare legs. This took place in the depths of a forest, at night, in winter, far from all human sight.

Suddenly a hand, which seemed to her enormous, seized the handle. A man had come up behind her. There are instincts for all moments in life. Cosette was not afraid.

"How old are you, little one?" asked the man.

"Eight, sir."

"Are you going far?"

"A good walk from here, sir."

The man said nothing for a moment, then he remarked abruptly,

"So you have no mother?"

"I don't know," answered the child.

"Who sent you to get water at such an hour?"

"It was Madame Thénardier. She keeps the inn."

As they neared the inn, Cosette timidly asked, "Will you let me take my bucket now? I am afraid that

if Madame sees that some one has carried it for me, she will beat me." The man handed her the bucket.

When the door opened Madame Thénardier appeared with a lighted candle in her hand, and agreed to give the traveler lodging.

That night, as the man was about to retire,

his eye fell upon the fireplace. There was no fire, but something attracted his gaze nevertheless.

It was Christmas Eve and two tiny children's shoes, pretty and graceful in shape, stood awaiting there beneath the chimney some sparkling gift from the good fairy. Madame Thénardier's own little daughters had set their

12—4th

shoes there and the fairy had already placed in each a shining gold piece.

The man was on the point of withdrawing, when he caught sight of another object. It was a wooden shoe, coarse, broken, and all covered with ashes and dried mud. It was Cosette's—Cosette, with the touching trust of childhood, had placed her shoe on the hearthstone also. There was nothing in this wooden shoe. The stranger fumbled in his waistcoat, bent over and placed a much larger coin in this shoe.

The next morning when Madame Thénardier handed the man his bill, he hardly glanced at it. His thoughts were evidently elsewhere.

"Madame," he inquired, "is business good here in Montfermeil?"

"So, so, Monsieur. We have many expenses. That child is costing us our very eyes,—Cosette, the Lark, as she is called hereabouts."

"What if I were to rid you of her?"

The landlady's red and ugly face brightened. "You will really take her away?"

"Immediately. Call her."

At this Madame Thénardier's husband stepped up. "Excuse me, sir, but one does not give away one's child."

The stranger took from his side pocket an old purse of black leather and drew out three bank-bills which he laid on the table. Then he said, "Go and fetch Cosette."

On waking up, Cosette had run to get her shoe. In it she had found the gold piece. She was dazzled. She guessed whence her gift had come. She hid the gold piece quickly in her pocket and hastily set about her morning duties. But as she swept the staircase she paused, forgetful of her broom and of the entire universe, and gazed at the star which was blazing at the bottom of her pocket. At this moment Madame Thénardier joined her.

"Cosette," she said almost gently, "come immediately."

Daylight was appearing when those of the inhabitants of Montfermeil who had begun to open their doors, beheld an old man leading a little girl dressed in mourning and carrying a pink doll in her arms, pass along the road to Paris. It was the man and Cosette. He had given her both the dress and the doll.

Cosette was going away. With whom? She did not know. Whither? She knew not. All that she understood was that she was leaving the Thénardier tavern behind her. No one had thought of bidding her farewell, nor had she thought of taking leave of any one.

Cosette walked along gravely, with her large eyes wide open, and gazing at the sky. She had put her gold coin in the pocket of her new apron. From time to time she bent down and looked at it; then she looked at the good man. She felt somewhat as though she were beside the good God.

From "Les Miserables." Adapted.

AN ORDER FOR A PICTURE

By Alice Cary

How many boys and girls like books well enough to read them at night by the light of a saucer of lard and a rag? This is what

Alice and Phœbe Cary did in their farm home near Cincinnati. As young children they had gone to a little country school a mile away, often lingering on the road home while an elder sister told them delightful tales. Now that school-days were over, not content with what they had learned, they made the most of the dozen odd volumes in their father's library. By the poor light of the lard saucer the two girls also wrote their earliest poems. Through life they lived and worked devotedly together. In 1849 they published jointly a book of poems, which made many friends for them among literary people in the East. A year later they resolved to meet some of these friends face to face. Whittier received them warmly in his Massachusetts home, these

> "Two song-birds wandering from their nest,
> A gray old farm-house in the West,"

as he called them later in his poem, *The Singer.* Horace Greeley became their stanch adviser. They settled in New York City, where they were much happier than they had been on their father's farm. They were lovable and bright in manner, brave and cheerful in spirit, and had, says Greeley, "the sunniest drawing-room, even by

gaslight, to be found between King's Bridge and the Battery."
They died in 1871, within a few months of each other.

Oh, good painter, tell me true,
    Has your hand the cunning to draw
     Shapes of things that you never saw?
Aye?   Well, here is an order for you.

Woods and corn-fields, a little brown,—
    The picture must not be over-bright,—
     Yet all in the golden and gracious light
Of a cloud, when the summer sun is down.
    Alway and alway, night and morn,
     Woods upon woods, with fields of corn
      Lying between them, not quite sear,
And not in the full, thick, leafy bloom,
When the wind can hardly find breathing-room
      Under their tassels,—cattle near,
Biting shorter the short green grass,
And a hedge of sumach and sassafras,
With bluebirds twittering all around,—
(Ah, good painter, you can't paint sound!)—
    These, and the little house where I was born,
Low and little, and black and old,
With children, many as it can hold,
All at the windows, open wide,—
Heads and shoulders clear outside,

And fair young faces all ablush:
    Perhaps you may have seen, some day,
    Roses crowding the self-same way,
Out of a wilding, wayside bush.

    Listen closer.   When you have done
        With woods and corn-fields and grazing herds,
    A lady, the loveliest ever the sun
Looked down upon you must paint for me:
Oh, if I only could make you see
    The clear blue eyes, the tender smile,
The sovereign sweetness, the gentle grace,
The woman's soul, and the angel's face
    That are beaming on me all the while,
        I need not speak these foolish words:
    Yet one word tells you all I would say,—
She is my mother: you will agree
That all the rest may be thrown away.

Two little urchins at her knee
You must paint, sir: one like me,—
    The other with a clearer brow,
    And the light of his adventurous eyes
    Flashing with boldest enterprise:
At ten years old he went to sea,—
    God knoweth if he be living now,—

He sailed in the good ship *Commodore,*
Nobody ever crossed her track
To bring us news, and she never came back.
    Ah, it is twenty long years and more
Since that old ship went out of the bay
        With my great-hearted brother on her deck:
        I watched him till he shrank to a speck,
    And his face was toward me all the way.
Bright his hair was, a golden brown,
    The time we stood at our mother's knee:
That beauteous head, if it did go down,
    Carried sunshine into sea!

Out in the fields one summer night
    We were together, half afraid
    Of the corn-leaves' rustling, and of the shade
        Of the high hills, stretching so still and far,—
Loitering till after the low little light
    Of the candle shone through the open door,
And over the hay-stack's pointed top,
All of a tremble and ready to drop,
        The first half-hour, the great yellow star,
That we, with staring, ignorant eyes,
Had often and often watched to see
    Propped and held in its place in the skies
By the fork of a tall red mulberry-tree,

Which close in the edge of our flax-field grew,—
Dead at the top,—just one branch full
Of leaves, notched round, and lined with wool,
From which it tenderly shook the dew
Over our heads, when we came to play
In its hand-breadth of shadow, day after day.

Afraid to go home, sir; for one of us bore
A nest full of speckled and thin-shelled eggs,—
The other, a bird, held fast by the legs,
Not so big as a straw of wheat:
The berries we gave her she wouldn't eat,
But cried and cried, till we held her bill,
So slim and shining, to keep her still.

At last we stood at our mother's knee;
Do you think, sir, if you try,
You can paint the look of a lie?
If you can, pray have the grace
To put it solely in the face
Of the urchin that is likest me:
I think 'twas solely mine, indeed:
But that's no matter,—paint it so;
The eyes of our mother—(take good heed)—
Looking not on the nestful of eggs,
Nor the fluttering bird, held so fast by the legs,
But straight through our faces down to our lies,
And, oh, with such injured, reproachful surprise!

I felt my heart bleed where that glance went, as
 though
A sharp blade struck through it. You, sir, know,
That you on the canvas are to repeat
Things that are fairest, things most sweet,—
Woods and corn-fields and mulberry-tree,—
The mother,—the lads, with their bird, at her knee:
 But, oh, that look of reproachful woe!
High as the heavens your name I'll shout,
If you paint me the picture, and leave that out.

ANSWER TO A CHILD'S QUESTION

By Samuel Taylor Coleridge

Do you ask what the birds say? The sparrow, the dove,
The linnet and thrush say, "I love, and I love!"
In the winter they're silent, the wind is so strong;
What it says I don't know, but it sings a loud song.
But green leaves, and blossoms, and sunny warm weather,
And singing and loving—all come back together.
But the lark is so brimful of gladness and love,
The green fields below him, the blue sky above,
That he sings, and he sings, and for ever sings he,
"I love my love and my love loves me."

THE WINNING OF THE SWORD
BY SIR THOMAS MALORY

When King Utherpendragon's son was born, came Merlin and said, "Sir, you must provide for the nourishing of your child."

"As thou wilt," said the king.

"Well," said Merlin, "I know a lord of yours, in this land, that is a passing true man and faithful, and he shall have the nourishing of your child. His name is Sir Ector, and he is a lord of fair livelihood. And let the child be delivered unto me at yonder gate unchristened." Then the king commanded two ladies to take the child, bound in rich cloth of gold, "And deliver him to the poor man you will meet at the gate of the castle." So the child was delivered unto Merlin, and so he bore it forth unto Sir Ector, and made an holy man to christen him, and named him Arthur.

Within two years King Uther fell sick of a great malady and died. Then stood the realm in great danger many years, for every lord that was mighty of men made him strong, and many thought to become king. Then Merlin went to the Archbishop of Canterbury, and counseled him to send for all the lords of the realm, and all the gentlemen of arms, to come to London before Christmas that God might show by a miracle who should rightly be king of the realm. So the Archbishop sent for all the lords and gentlemen of arms, and many of them made their lives clean that their prayers might be more acceptable to God.

So in the greatest church of London when the first mass was done, there was seen in the churchyard, against the high altar, a great stone, four-square, like a marble stone, and in the midst thereof was an anvil of steel, a foot high, and therein stuck a fair sword, naked, to the point, and letters of gold were written about the sword that said: "Whoso pulleth out this sword from this stone and anvil is rightly born king of England."

So all the lords went to behold the stone and the sword, and when they saw the writing, some tried, such as wished to be king; but none might stir the sword, nor move it.

"He is not yet here," said the archbishop, "that shall win the sword, but doubt not God will make him known. But this is my counsel," said the archbishop, "that we find ten knights, men of good fame, to watch over this sword." And so it was ordained that every man that would, should try to win the sword. And upon New

Year's Day, the barons made a joust and tournament, that all knights that would joust and tourney there might play; and all this was ordained to keep the lords together, and the commons, for the archbishop trusted that God would make him known that should win the sword.

So, upon the New Year's Day, when the service was done, the barons rode to the field, some to joust, and some to tourney. And it happened that Sir Ector rode to the jousts, and with him rode Sir Kaye, his son, and young Arthur, that was his foster brother. As they rode towards the jousts, Sir Kaye missed his sword, for he had left it at his father's lodging; and so he prayed young Arthur to ride back for his sword.

"With a good will," said Arthur, and rode back fast after the sword; and when he came home the lady and all were gone out to see the jousting. Then said Arthur to himself, "I will ride to the churchyard and take the sword with me that sticketh in the stone, for my brother, Sir Kaye, shall not be without a sword this day." And so, when he came to the churchyard, Arthur alighted, and tied his horse to the stile, and found no knights there, for they were all at the jousting; and he took the sword by the handle, and lightly and fiercely he pulled it out of the stone, and took his horse, and rode his way till he came to his brother, Sir Kaye, and delivered him the sword.

As soon as Sir Kaye saw the sword he knew well that

it was the sword of the stone; and so he rode to his father, Sir Ector, and said, "Sir, lo! here is the sword of the stone; wherefore I must be king of this land." When Sir Ector beheld the sword, he returned to the church, and there they alighted all three, and went into the church; and anon he made Sir Kaye swear upon a book how he came by the sword.

"Sir," said Sir Kaye, "my brother, Arthur, he brought it to me."

"How got you this sword?" said Sir Ector to Arthur.

"Sir, I will tell you; when I came home for my brother's sword I found nobody at home to deliver me his sword; and so I thought my brother, Sir Kaye, should not be swordless, and I came thither eagerly, and pulled it out of the stone."

"Now," said Sir Ector to Arthur, "I understand that you must be king of this land."

"Wherefore I?" said Arthur, "and for what cause?"

"Sir," said Sir Ector, "God will have it so. Now, let me see whether ye can put the sword there as it was."

"That is no mastery," said Arthur; and so he put it in the stone. Therewith Sir Ector tried to pull out the sword and failed.

"Now try you," said Sir Ector to Sir Kaye. And anon Sir Kaye pulled at the sword with all his might, but it would not come.

"Now shall ye try," said Sir Ector to Arthur.

"With a good will," said Arthur, and pulled it out easily. And therewith Sir Ector kneeled down to the earth, and Sir Kaye also.

"Alas!" said Arthur, "mine own dear father, and my brother, why kneel you to me?"

"Nay, nay, my Lord Arthur. I was never your father, nor of your blood. I now know well that you are of an higher blood than I thought you were." And then Sir Ector told him all, how he had taken him to nourish, and by whose commandment, and at Merlin's hand. Then Arthur made great moan when he understood that Sir Ector was not his father.

"Sir," said Sir Ector unto Arthur, "will you be my good and gracious lord when you are king?"

"Else were I to blame," said Arthur, "for you are the man in the world that I am the most beholden unto, and my good lady and mother, your wife, that, as well as her own, hath fostered and kept me; and, if ever it be God's will that I be king, as you say, ye shall desire of me what I may do, and I shall not fail you; God forbid I should fail you."

"Sir," said Sir Ector, "I will ask no more of you but that you will make my son, your foster brother, Sir Kaye, steward of all your lands."

"That shall be done, sir," said Arthur, "and more, by the faith of my body, and never man shall have that office but him while he and I live." Therewith they went unto the archbishop, and told him how the sword was won, and by whom.

And so anon was the coronation held, and there was Arthur sworn to the lords and commons to be a true king, to stand with true justice from thenceforth all the days of his life; and then he made all the lords that had held off the crown to come in and do him service as they ought to do. And many complaints were made unto King Arthur of great wrongs that were done since the death of King Utherpendragon, of many lands that were bereaved of lords, knights, ladies, and gentlemen; wherefore King Arthur made the lands to be rendered again unto them that owned them.

When this was done, and the king had established all the countries about London, then he did make Sir Kaye steward of England, and Sir Ulfias was made chamberlain. Within a few years after, King Arthur won all the north. A part of Wales held against him, but he overcame them all, and all through the noble prowess of himself and his knights of the Round Table.

Adapted.

And slowly answered Arthur from the barge:
"The old order changeth, yielding place to new,
And God fulfils Himself in many ways,
Lest one good custom should corrupt the world."

From "Idylls of the King." Alfred, Lord Tennyson.

INCIDENT OF THE FRENCH CAMP

By Robert Browning

You know, we French stormed Ratisbon:
 A mile or so away,
On a little mound, Napoleon
 Stood on our storming-day;
With neck out-thrust, you fancy how,
 Legs wide, arms locked behind,
As if to balance the prone brow
 Oppressive with its mind.

Just as perhaps he mused, "My plans
 That soar, to earth may fall,
Let once my army-leader, Lannes,
 Waver at yonder wall,"—
Out 'twixt the battery-smokes there flew
 A rider, bound on bound
Full-galloping; nor bridle drew
 Until he reached the mound.

Then off there flung in smiling joy,
 And held himself erect
By just his horse's mane, a boy:
 You hardly could suspect—

ON A LITTLE MOUND NAPOLEON STOOD

13—4th

(So tight he kept his lips compressed
    Scarce any blood came through),
You looked twice ere you saw his breast
    Was all but shot in two.

"Well," cried he, "Emperor, by God's grace
    We've got you Ratisbon!
The marshal's in the market-place,
    And you'll be there anon
To see your flag-bird flap his vans
    Where I, to heart's desire,
Perched him!" The chief's eye flashed; his plans
    Soared up again like fire.

The chief's eye flashed; but presently
    Softened itself, as sheathes
A film the mother-eagle's eye
    When her bruised eaglet breathes;
"You're wounded!" "Nay," the soldier's pride
    Touched to the quick, he said:
"I'm killed, Sire!" and his chief beside,
    Smiling the boy fell dead.

The characteristic of a genuine heroism is its persistency. All men have wandering impulses, fits and starts of generosity. It was a high council that I once heard given to a young person: "Always do what you are afraid to do." *From the essay "Heroism." Ralph Waldo Emerson.*

JOAN OF ARC

By Andrew Lang

Nearly five hundred years ago, the children of Domremy, a little village near the Meuse, on the borders of France and Lorraine, used to meet and dance and sing beneath a beautiful beech-tree. They called it "The Fairy Tree," or "The Good Ladies' Lodge," meaning the fairies by the words "Good Ladies." Among these children was one named Joan, (born in 1412), the daughter of an honest farmer. It was said among the villagers that Joan's godmother had once seen the fairies dancing; but though some of the older people believed in the Good Ladies, it does not seem that Joan and the other children had faith in them or thought much about them. They only went to the tree and to a neighboring fairy well to eat cakes and laugh and play.

Joan was good and simple, and was often in churches and holy places. And when she heard the church bell ring, she would kneel down in the fields. All those who had seen Joan told the same tale. She was always kind, simple, industrious, pious, and yet merry, and fond of playing with the others round the fairy tree. They say that the singing birds came to her and nestled in her breast.

When Joan was between twelve and thirteen, so she declared, *a Voice came to her from God for her guidance,* but when first it came, she was in great fear. And it came, that Voice, about noonday, in the summer season, she being in her father's garden.

It was in 1424 that the Voices first came to Joan the Maid. The years went on, bringing more and more sorrow to France. In 1428 only a very few small towns in the east held out for the Dauphin, and these were surrounded on every side by enemies. Meanwhile the Voices came more frequently, urging Joan to go into France and help her country. She asked how she, a girl, who could not ride or use sword or lance, could be of any help. Rather would she stay at home and spin beside her dear mother. At the same time she was encouraged by a vague old prophecy "that France was to be saved by a maiden from the Oak Wood," and there was an oak wood near Domremy.

Some such prophecy had an influence on Joan, and probably helped people to believe in her. The Voices, moreover, instantly and often commanded her to go to Vaucouleurs, a neighboring town which was loyal, and there meet Robert de Baudricourt, who was captain of the French garrison. It was to him that Joan must go, a country girl to a great noble, and tell him that she, and she alone, could save France!

Joan came, in her simple red dress, and walked straight up to the captain among his men. She told him that the Dauphin must keep quiet, and risk no battle, for before the middle of Lent next year God would send him succor.

She added that the kingdom belonged, not to the Dauphin, but to her Master, who willed that the Dauphin should be crowned, and she herself would lead him to Reims, to be anointed with the holy oil.

"And who is your Master?" said Robert.

"The King of Heaven."

Robert, very naturally, thought Joan was crazed, and shrugged his shoulders. He bluntly told a bystander to box her ears, and take her back to her father.

But the time at last drew near when she had prophesied that the Dauphin was to receive help from Heaven— namely, in the Lent of 1429.

Early in January, 1429, Joan the Maid turned her back on Domremy, which she was never to see again. She went to Vaucouleurs and stayed with a friend. On the twelfth of February, the story goes that she went to Robert de Baudricourt.

"You delay too long," she said. "On this very day, at Orleans, the gentle Dauphin has lost a battle."

This was, in fact, the Battle of Herrings, so called because the English defeated and cut off a French and Scottish force which attacked them as they were bringing herrings into camp for provisions in Lent. If this tale is true, Joan can not have known of the battle by any common means.

Now the people of Vaucouleurs bought clothes for Joan to wear on her journey to the Dauphin. They were such clothes as men wore—doublet, hose, surcoat, boots, and spurs—and Robert de Baudricourt gave Joan a sword.

On the sixth of March Joan arrived at Chinon, where for two or three days the King's advisers would not let her see him. At last they yielded, and she went straight up to him, and when he denied that he was the King, she told him that she knew well who he was.

"This is the King," said Charles, pointing to a richly dressed noble.

"No, fair Sire. You are he!"

Still, it was not easy to believe. Joan stayed at Chinon in the house of a noble lady. The young Duc d'Alencon was on her side from the first, bewitched by her noble horsemanship which she had never learned. Great people came to see her, but when she was alone she wept and prayed. The King sent messengers to inquire about her at Domremy, but time was going and Orleans was not relieved.

Joan was wear of being asked questions. One day she went to Charles and said: "Gentle Dauphin, why do you delay to believe me? I tell you that God has taken pity on you and your people. And I will tell you, by your leave, something which will show you that you should believe me."

Then she told him secretly something which, as he said, none could know but God and himself. A few months later, in July, a man about the court wrote a letter, in which he declares that none knows what Joan told the King, but he was plainly as glad as if something had been revealed to him by the Holy Spirit.

The King to whom Joan brought this wonderful message, the King whom she loved so loyally, and for whom she died, spoiled all her plans. He, with his political advisers, prevented her from driving the English quite out of France.

These favorites found their profit in dawdling and delaying, as politicians generally do. Joan had literally to goad them into action, to drag them on by constant prayers and tears. They were lazy, comfortable, cowardly, disbelieving; in their hearts they hated the Maid, who put them to so much trouble.

As for Charles, to whom the Maid was so loyal, had he been a man like the Black Prince, Joan would have led him into Paris before the summer was ended. "I shall only last one year and a little more," she often said to the King. The Duc d'Alencon heard her, but much of that precious year was wasted.

The King made up his mind at last. Jean and Pierre, Joan's brothers, were to ride with her to Orleans. The King gave Joan armor and horses, and offered her a sword. But her Voices told her that behind the altar of St. Catherine at Fierbois, there was an old sword, with five crosses on the blade, buried in the earth. That sword she was to wear. A man whom Joan did not know, and had

never seen, was sent from Tours, and found the sword in
the place which she described.

And so Joan went to war. She led, she says, ten or
twelve thousand soldiers. Joan was then seventeen.
About half-past six in the morning the fight against
Orleans began. The French and Scottish leaped into the
foss, they set ladders against the walls, they reached the
battlements, and were struck down by English swords and
axes. Cannon-balls and great stones and arrows rained on
them. "Fight on!" cried the Maid, "the place is ours."

At one o'clock she set a ladder against the wall with
her own hands, but was deeply wounded by an arrow,
which pierced clean through between neck and shoulder.
Joan wept, but seizing the arrow with her own hands she
dragged it out. "Yet," says Dunois, "she did not with-
draw from the battle, nor take any medicine for the
wound; and the onslaught lasted from morning till eight
at night, so that there was no hope of victory. Then
I desired that the army should go back to the town, but
the Maid came to me and bade me wait a little longer.

"Next she mounted her horse and rode into a vineyard,
and there prayed for the space of seven minutes or eight.
Then she returned, took her banner, and stood on the
brink of the foss. The English trembled when they saw
her, but our men returned to the charge and met with no
resistance. The English fled or were slain, and we
went back gladly into Orleans."

SO JOAN WENT TO WAR

The success of the Maid seemed a miracle to the world.
Yet the King of France loitered about the castles of the
Loire with his favorites and his adviser, the Archbishop of
Reims. They wasted the one year of Joan. At last,
with difficulty, Charles was brought to visit Reims, and to
consent to be crowned like his ancestors. He was crowned
and anointed with the Holy Oil. The Twelve Peers of
France were not all present—some were on the English
side—but Joan stood by Charles, her banner in her hand.
"It bore the brunt, and deserved to share the renown,"
she said later to her accusers.

When the ceremony was ended and the Dauphin Charles
was crowned and anointed King, the Maid knelt weeping
at his feet.

"Gentle King," she said, "now is accomplished the will
of God, who desired that you should come to Reims to be
consecrated, and to prove that you are the true King and
that the kingdom is yours."

Then all the knights wept for joy.

The King bade Joan choose her reward. Already horses,
rich armor, jeweled daggers, had been given to her.
These, adding to the beauty and the glory of her aspect,
had made men follow her more gladly, and for that she
valued them. She, too, made gifts to noble ladies, and
gave much to the poor. She only wanted money to wage
the war with, not for herself. Her family was made noble; on its shield, between two lilies, a sword upholds

the crown.   Her father was at Reims, and saw her in her glory.   What reward, then, was Joan to choose?   She chose nothing for herself, but that her native village of Domremy should be free from taxes.   The news her father carried home from the splendid scene at Reims.

"Would to God, my Maker," said Joan, "that I might now depart and lay down my arms and help my father and mother, and keep their sheep with my brothers and sisters, who would rejoice to see me."

The politicians triumphed.   They thwarted the Maid, they made her promise to take Paris of no avail.   They destroyed the confidence of men in the banner that had never gone back.   Now they might take their ease.   Now they might loiter in the gardens of the Loire.   The Maid had failed, by their design, and by their cowardice.   The treachery that she, who feared nothing else, had long dreaded, was accomplished.

About her trial and death, I have not the heart to write a long story.   Enough.   They burned Joan the Maid. Even the English wept, even a secretary of the English king said that they had burned a saint.   But it profited the English not at all.   "Though they ceased not to be brave," says Patrick Abercromby, a Scot, "yet they were almost on all occasions defeated, and within the short space of twenty-two years lost not only all the conquests made by them in little less than a hundred, but also the inheritance which they had enjoyed for above three centuries."

Abridged.

THE PIED PIPER OF HAMELIN

By Robert Browning

I

Hamelin Town's in Brunswick,
By famous Hanover city;
    The river Weser, deep and wide,
    Washes its wall on the southern side;
    A pleasanter spot you never spied;
But, when begins my ditty,
    Almost five hundred years ago,
    To see the townsfolk suffer so
        From vermin, was a pity.

II

Rats!
They fought the dogs and killed the cats,
    And bit the babies in the cradles,
And ate the cheeses out of the vats,
    And licked the soup from the cooks' own ladles,
Split open the kegs of salted sprats,
Made nests inside men's Sunday hats,
And even spoiled the women's chats
    By drowning their speaking
        With shriek and squeaking
In fifty different sharps and flats.

III

At last the people in a body
    To the Town Hall came flocking:
  "'Tis clear," cried they, "our Mayor's a noddy;
    And as for our Corporation—shocking
    To think we buy gowns lined with ermine
    For dolts that can't or won't determine
    What's best to rid us of our vermin!
    You hope, because you're old and obese,
    To find in the furry civic robe ease?
Rouse up, sirs! Give your brains a racking
To find the remedy we're lacking,
    Or, sure as fate, we'll send you packing!"
At this the Mayor and Corporation
Quaked with a mighty consternation.

IV

An hour they sat in council;
    At length the Mayor broke silence:
    "For a guilder I'd my ermine gown sell,
    I wish I were a mile hence!
It's easy to bid one rack one's brain—
I'm sure my poor head aches again,
I've scratched it so, and all in vain.
Oh for a trap, a trap, a trap!"
Just as he said this, what should hap

At the chamber-door but a gentle tap?
"Bless us," cried the Mayor, "what's that?"
(With the Corporation as he sat,
Looking little though wondrous fat;
Nor brighter was his eye, nor moister
Than a too-long-opened oyster,
Save when at noon his paunch grew mutinous
For a plate of turtle, green and glutinous)
"Only a scraping of shoes on the mat?
Anything like the sound of a rat
Makes my heart go pit-a-pat!"

V

"Come in!"—the Mayor cried, looking bigger:
And in did come the strangest figure!
His queer long coat from heel to head
Was half of yellow and half of red,
And he himself was tall and thin,
With sharp blue eyes, each like a pin,
And light loose hair, yet swarthy skin,
No tuft on cheek nor beard on chin,
But lips where smiles went out and in;
There was no guessing his kith and kin:
And nobody could enough admire
The tall man and his quaint attire.
Quoth one: "It's as my great grand-sire,

Starting up at the Trump of Doom's tone,
Had walked this way from his painted tombstone!"

VI

He advanced to the council-table:
And, "Please your honors," said he, "I'm able,
By means of a secret charm, to draw
All creatures living beneath the sun,
That creep or swim or fly or run,
After me so as you never saw!
And I chiefly use my charm
On creatures that do people harm,
The mole and toad, and newt and viper;
And people call me the Pied Piper."
(And here they noticed round his neck
A scarf of red and yellow stripe,
To match with his coat of the self-same check;
And at the scarf's end hung a pipe;
And his fingers, they noticed, were ever straying
As if impatient to be playing
Upon this pipe, as low it dangled
Over his vesture so old-fangled.)
"Yet," said he, "poor piper as I am,
In Tartary I freed the Cham,
Last June, from his huge swarms of gnats;
I eased in Asia the Nizam

Of a monstrous brood of vampire-bats:
And as for what your brain bewilders,
If I can rid your town of rats
Will you give me a thousand guilders?"
"One? fifty thousand!"—was the exclamation
Of the astonished Mayor and Corporation.

VII

Into the street the Piper stept,
　　Smiling first a little smile,
As if he knew what magic slept
　　In his quiet pipe the while;
Then, like a musical adept,
To blow the pipe his lips he wrinkled,
And green and blue his sharp eyes twinkled,
Like a candle-flame where salt is sprinkled;
And ere three shrill notes the pipe uttered,
You heard as if an army muttered;
And the muttering grew to a grumbling;
And the grumbling grew to a mighty rumbling;
And out of the houses the rats came tumbling.
Great rats, small rats, lean rats, brawny rats,
Brown rats, black rats, gray rats, tawny rats,
Grave old plodders, gay young friskers,
　　Fathers, mothers, uncles, cousins,
Cocking tails and pricking whiskers,

Families by tens and dozens,
Brothers, sisters, husbands, wives—
Followed the Piper for their lives.
From street to street he piped advancing,
And step for step they followed dancing,
Until they came to the river Weser,
Wherein all plunged and perished!
—Save one who, stout as Julius Cæsar,
Swam across and lived to carry
(As he, the manuscript he cherished)
To Rat-land home his commentary:
Which was, "At the first shrill notes of the pipe.
I heard a sound as of scraping tripe,
And putting apples, wondrous ripe,
Into a cider-press's gripe:
And a moving away of pickle-tub-boards,
And a leaving ajar of conserve-cupboards,
And a drawing the corks of train-oil-flasks,
And a breaking the hoops of butter-casks;
And it seemed as if a voice
(Sweeter far than by harp or by psaltery
Is breathed) called out, 'Oh rats, rejoice!
The world is grown to one vast drysaltery!
So munch on, crunch on, take your nuncheon,
Breakfast, supper, dinner, luncheon!'
And just as a bulky sugar-puncheon,
All ready staved, like a great sun shone

14—4th

Glorious scarce an inch before me,
Just as methought it said, 'Come, bore me!'
—I found the Weser rolling o'er me."

VIII

You should have heard the Hamelin people
Ringing the bells till they rocked the steeple.
"Go," cried the Mayor, "and get long poles,
Poke out the nests and block up the holes!
Consult with carpenters and builders,
And leave in our town not even a trace
Of the rats!"—When suddenly, up the face
Of the Piper perked in the market-place,
With a, "First, if you please, my thousand guilders!"

IX

A thousand guilders!   The Mayor looked blue;
So did the Corporation, too.
For council dinners made rare havoc
With Claret, Moselle, Vin-de-Grave, Hock;
And half the money would replenish
Their cellar's biggest butt with Rhenish.
To pay this sum to a wandering fellow
With a Gipsy coat of red and yellow!
"Beside," quoth the Mayor with a knowing wink,
"Our business was done at the river's brink;

We saw with our eyes the vermin sink,
And what's dead can't come to life, I think.
So, friend, we're not the folks to shrink
From the duty of giving you something for **drink,**
And a matter of money to put in your poke;
But as for the guilders, what we spoke
Of them, as you very well know, was in joke.
Beside, our losses have made us thrifty.
A thousand guilders!   Come, take fifty!"

X

The Piper's face fell, and he cried,
"No trifling!   I can't wait, beside!
I've promised to visit by dinner time
Bagdad, and accept the prime
Of the Head-Cook's pottage, all he's rich **in,**
For having left, in the Caliph's kitchen,
Of a nest of scorpions no survivor:
With him I proved no bargain-driver,
With you, don't think I'll bate a stiver!
And folks who put me in a passion
May find me pipe after another fashion."

XI

"How?" cried the Mayor, "d'ye think I brook
Being worse treated than a Cook?

Insulted by a lazy ribald
With idle pipe and vesture piebald?
You threaten us, fellow?   Do your worst,
Blow your pipe there till you burst!"

XII

Once more he stept into the street,
    And to his lips again
Laid his long pipe of smooth straight cane;
    And ere he blew three notes (such sweet
Soft notes as yet musician's cunning
    Never gave the enraptured air)
There was a rustling that seemed like a bustling
Of merry crowds justling at pitching and hust-
      ling;
Small feet were pattering, wooden shoes clattering,
Little hands clapping and little tongues chattering,
And, like fowls in a farm-yard when barley is scatter-
      ing,
    Out came the children running.
All the little boys and girls,
With rosy cheeks and flaxen curls,
And sparkling eyes and teeth like pearls,
Tripping and skipping, ran merrily after
The wonderful music with shouting and laughter.

TRIPPING AND SKIPPING, RAN MERRILY AFTER

XIII

The Mayor was dumb, and the Council stood
As if they were changed into blocks of wood,
Unable to move a step, or cry
To the children merrily skipping by,
—Could only follow with the eye
That joyous crowd at the Piper's back.
But how the Mayor was on the rack,
And the wretched Council's bosoms beat,
As the Piper turned from the High Street
To where the Weser rolled its waters
Right in the way of their sons and daughters!
However, he turned from South to West,
And to Koppelberg Hill his steps addressed,
And after him the children pressed;
Great was the joy in every breast.
"He never can cross that mighty top!
He's forced to let the piping drop,
And we shall see our children stop!"
When, lo, as they reached the mountain-side,
A wondrous portal opened wide,
As if a cavern was suddenly hollowed;
And the Piper advanced and the children followed,
And when all were in to the very last,
The door in the mountain-side shut fast.
Did I say all? No! One was lame,

And could not dance the whole of the way;
And in after years, if you would blame
His sadness, he was used to say,—
"It's dull in our town since my playmates left!
I can't forget that I'm bereft
Of all the pleasant sights they see,
Which the Piper also promised me.
For he led us, he said, to a joyous land,
Joining the town and just at hand,
Where waters gushed and fruit-trees grew
And flowers put forth a fairer hue,
And everything was strange and new;
The sparrows were brighter than peacocks here,
And their dogs outran our fallow deer,
And honey-bees had lost their stings,
And horses were born with eagles' wings:
And just as I became assured
My lame foot would be speedily cured,
The music stopped and I stood still,
And found myself outside the hill,
Left alone against my will,
To go now limping as before,
And never hear of that country more!"

XIV

Alas, alas for Hamelin!
        There came into many a burgher's pate

A text which says that Heaven's gate
Opes to the rich at as easy rate
As the needle's eye takes a camel in!
The Mayor sent East, West, North and South,
To offer the Piper, by word of mouth,
          Wherever it was men's lot to find him,
Silver and gold to his heart's content,
If he'd only return the way he went,
          And bring the children behind him.
But when they saw 'twas a lost endeavor,
And Piper and dancers were gone for ever,
They made a decree that lawyers never
          Should think their records dated duly
If, after the day of the month and year,
These words did not as well appear,
"And so long after what happened here
          On the Twenty-second of July,
Thirteen hundred and seventy-six:"
And the better in memory to fix
The place of the children's last retreat,
They called it, the Pied Piper's Street—
Where any one playing on pipe or tabor
Was sure for the future to lose his labor.
Nor suffered they hostelry or tavern
          To shock with mirth a street so solemn;
But opposite the place of the cavern,
          They wrote the story on a column,

And on the great church-window painted
The same, to make the world acquainted
How their children were stolen away,
And there it stands to this very day.
And I must not omit to say
That in Transylvania there's a tribe
Of alien people who ascribe
The outlandish ways and dress
On which their neighbors lay such stress,
To their fathers and mothers having risen
Out of some subterraneous prison
Into which they were trepanned
Long time ago in a mighty band
Out of Hamelin Town in Brunswick land,
But how or why, they don't understand.

XV

So, Willy, let me and you be wipers
Of scores out with all men—especially pipers!
And, whether they pipe us free from rats or from mice,
If we've promised them aught, let us keep our promise!

To thine own self be true;
And it must follow, as the night the day,
Thou canst not then be false to any man.

From "Hamlet." William Shakespeare.

THE GRIFFIN AND THE MINOR CANON

By Frank R. Stockton

In this delightful story Stockton imagines a strange beast called a Griffin learning that a stone image of himself is carved over the door of a church in a certain town. Led by curiosity he visits the town and remains hours before the church gazing at the image. Day after day he returns to this post. The townsfolk are greatly frightened. The Minor Canon, the gentle young minister and schoolmaster of the place, alone is brave enough to talk to the monster. The people know that the Griffin eats only twice a year, one time being at the autumnal equinox. As this draws near their fear increases. Finally they beg the young minister to leave the town, hoping that the Griffin will follow him. This the minister consents to do.

When the Griffin found that the Minor Canon had left the town he seemed sorry, but showed no desire to go and look for him. After a few days had passed he became much annoyed, and asked some of the people where the Minor Canon had gone. But, although the citizens had been so anxious that the young clergyman should go to the dreadful wilds, thinking that the Griffin would immediately follow him, they were now afraid to mention the Minor Canon's destination, for the monster seemed angry already, and if he should suspect their trick he would, doubtless, become very much enraged.

So every one said he did not know, and the Griffin wandered about disconsolate. One morning he looked into the Minor Canon's school-house, which was always empty now, and thought that it was a shame that everything should suffer on account of the young man's absence.

"It does not matter so much about the church," he said, "for nobody went there; but it is a pity about the school.   I think I will teach it myself until he returns."

It was the hour for opening the school, and the Griffin went inside and pulled the rope which rang the school bell.   Some of the children who heard the bell ran to see what was the matter, supposing it to be a joke of one of their companions; but when they saw the Griffin they stood astonished and scared.

"Go tell the other pupils," said the monster, "that school is about to open, and that if they are not all here in ten minutes I shall come after them."

In seven minutes every child was in place.

Never was seen such an orderly school.   Not a boy or girl uttered a whisper.   The Griffin climbed into the master's seat, his wide wings spread on each side of him, because he could not lean back in his chair while they stuck out behind, and his great tail coiled around, in front of the desk, the barbed end sticking up, ready to tap any boy or girl who might misbehave.

The Griffin now addressed the pupils, telling them that he intended to teach them while their master was away. In speaking he tried to imitate, as far as possible, the mild and gentle tones of the Minor Canon; but it must be admitted that in this he was not very successful.

He had paid quite a good deal of attention to the studies of the school, and he determined not to try to teach the children anything new, but to review them in what they had been studying; so he called up the various classes, and questioned them upon their previous lessons. The children racked their brains to remember what they had learned. They were so afraid of the Griffin's displeasure that they recited as they had never recited before. One of the boys, far down in his class, answered so well that the Griffin was astonished.

"I should think you would be at the head," said he. "I am sure you have never been in the habit of reciting so well. Why is this?"

"Because I did not choose to take the trouble," said the boy, trembling in his boots. He felt obliged to speak the truth, for all the children thought that the great eyes of the Griffin could see right through them, and that he would know when they told a falsehood.

"You ought to be ashamed of yourself," said the Griffin. "Go down to the very tail of the class; and if you are not at the head in two days, I shall know the reason why."

The next afternoon this boy was Number One.

It was astonishing how much these children now learned of what they had been studying. It was as if they had been educated over again. The Griffin used no severity toward them, but there was a look about him which made them unwilling to go to bed until they were sure they knew their lessons for the next day.

The Griffin now thought that he ought to visit the sick and the poor; and he began to go about the town for this purpose. The effect upon the sick was miraculous. All, except those who were very ill, indeed, jumped from their beds when they heard he was coming; and declared themselves quite well.

To those who could not get up he gave herbs and roots, which none of them had ever before thought of as medicines, but which the Griffin had seen used in various parts of the world; and most of them recovered. But, for all that, they afterward said that, no matter what happened to them, they hoped they should never again have such a doctor coming to their bedsides, feeling their pulses and looking at their tongues.

As for the poor, they seemed to have utterly disappeared. All those who had depended upon charity for their daily bread were now at work in some way or other; many of them offering to do odd jobs for their neighbors just for the sake of their meals—a thing which before had been seldom heard of in the town. The Griffin could find no one who needed his assistance.

The summer had now passed, and the autumnal equinox was rapidly approaching. The citizens were in a state of great alarm and anxiety. The Griffin showed no signs of going away, but seemed to have settled himself permanently among them. In a short time the day for his semi-annual meal would arrive, and then what would happen? The monster would certainly be very hungry, and would devour all their children.

Now they greatly regretted and lamented that they had sent away the Minor Canon; he was the only one on whom they could have depended in this trouble, for he could talk freely with the Griffin, and so find out what could be done. But it would not do to be inactive. Some step must be taken immediately.

A meeting of the citizens was called, and two old men were appointed to go and talk with the Griffin. They were instructed to offer to prepare a splendid dinner for him on equinox day—one which would entirely satisfy his hunger. They would offer him the fattest mutton, the most tender beef, fish, and game of various sorts, and anything of the kind that he might fancy. If none of these suited, they were to mention that there was an orphan asylum in the next town.

"Anything would be better," said the citizens, "than to have our poor children devoured."

The old men went to the Griffin; but their propositions were not received with favor.

"From what I have seen of the people of this town," said the monster, "I do not think I could relish anything which was prepared by them. They appear to be all cowards, and, therefore, mean and selfish. As for eating one of them, old or young, I could not think of it for a moment. In fact, there was only one creature in the whole place for whom I could have had any appetite, and that is the Minor Canon, who has gone away. He was brave, and good, and honest, and I think I should have relished him."

"Ah!" said one of the old men very politely, "in that case I wish we had not sent him to the dreadful wilds!"

"What!" cried the Griffin. "What do you mean? Explain instantly what you are talking about!"

The old man, terribly frightened at what he had said, was obliged to tell how the Minor Canon had been sent away by the people, in the hope that the Griffin might be induced to follow him.

When the monster heard this he became furiously angry. He dashed away from the old men, and spreading his wings, flew backward and forward over the town. He was so much excited that his tail became red-hot, and glowed like a meteor against the evening sky.

When at last he settled down in the little field where he usually rested, and thrust his tail into the brook, the steam arose like a cloud, and the water of the stream ran hot through the town. The citizens were greatly frightened, and bitterly blamed the old man for telling about the Minor Canon.

"It is plain," they said, "that the Griffin intended at last to go and look for him, and we should have been saved. Now who can tell what misery you have brought upon us!"

The Griffin did not remain long in the little field. As soon as his tail was cool he flew to the town-hall and rang the bell. The citizens knew that they were expected to come there; and although they were afraid to go, they were still more afraid to stay away, and they crowded into the hall. The Griffin was on the platform at one end, flapping his wings and walking up and down, and the end of his tail was still so warm that it slightly scorched the boards as he dragged it after him.

When everybody who was able to come was there, the Griffin stood still and addressed the meeting.

"I have had a very low opinion of you," he said, "ever since I discovered what cowards you are, but I had no idea that you were so ungrateful, selfish, and cruel as I now find you to be. Here was your Minor Canon, who labored day and night for your good, and thought of nothing else but how he might benefit you and make you happy; and as soon as you imagine yourselves threatened with a danger —for well I know you are dreadfully afraid of me—you send him off, caring not whether he returns or perishes, hoping thereby to save yourselves.

"Now, I had conceived a great liking for that young man, and had intended, in a day or two, to go and look him up. But I have changed my mind about him. I shall go and find him, but I shall send him back here to live among you, and I intend that he shall enjoy the reward of his labor and his sacrifices.

"Go, some of you, to the officers of the church, who ran away when I first came here, and tell them never to return to this town under penalty of death. And if, when your Minor Canon comes back to you, you do not bow yourselves before him, put him in the highest place among you, and serve and honor him all his life, beware of my terrible vengeance! There were only two good things in this town: the Minor Canon and the stone image of myself over your church door. One of these you have sent away, and the other I shall carry away myself."

With these words he dismissed the meeting, and it was time, for the end of his tail had become so hot that there was danger of its setting fire to the building.

The next morning the Griffin came to the church, and tearing the stone image of himself from its fastenings over the great door, he grasped it with his powerful forelegs and flew up into the air. Then, after hovering over the town for a moment, he gave his tail an angry shake and took up his flight to the dreadful wilds.

When he reached this desolate region, he set the stone griffin upon the ledge of a rock which rose in front of the dismal cave he called his home. There the image occupied a position somewhat similar to that it had had over the church door; and the Griffin, panting with the exertion of carrying such an enormous load to so great a distance,

15—4th

lay down upon the ground and regarded it with much satisfaction.

When he felt somewhat rested he went to look for the Minor Canon. He found the young man, weak and half-starved, lying under the shadow of a rock. After picking him up and carrying him to his cave, the Griffin flew away to a distant marsh, where he procured some roots and herbs which he well knew were strengthening and beneficial to man, though he had never tasted them himself. After eating these the Minor Canon was greatly revived, and sat up and listened while the Griffin told him what had happened in the town.

" Do you know," said the monster, when he had finished, " that I have had, and still have, a great liking for you?"

"I am very glad to hear it," said the Minor Canon, with his usual politeness.

"I am not at all sure that you would be," said the Griffin, "if you thoroughly understood the state of the case; but we will not consider that now. If some things were different, other things would be otherwise. I have been so enraged by discovering the manner in which you have been treated that I have determined that you shall at last enjoy the rewards and honors to which you are entitled. Lie down and have a good sleep, and then I will take you back to the town."

As he heard these words a look of trouble came over the young man's face.

"You need not give yourself any anxiety," said the Griffin, "about my return to the town.   I shall not remain there.   Now that I have that admirable likeness of my-self in front of my cave, where I can sit at my leisure and gaze upon its noble features, I have no wish to see that abode of cowardly and selfish people."

The Minor Canon, relieved from his fears, lay back and dropped into a doze; and when he was sound asleep the Griffin took him up, and carried him back to the town. He arrived just before daybreak, and putting the young man gently on the grass in the little field where he him-self used to rest, the monster, without having been seen by any of the people, flew back to his home.

When the Minor Canon made his appearance in the morning among the citizens, the enthusiasm and cordiality with which he was received were truly wonderful.   He was taken to a house which had been occupied by one of the banished high officers of the place, and every one was anxious to do all that could be done for his health and comfort.

The people crowded into the church when he held ser-vices, so that the three old women who used to be his week-day congregation could not get to the best seats, which they had always been in the habit of taking; and the parents of the bad children determined to reform them at home, in order that he might be spared the trouble of keeping up his former school.   The Minor Canon was appointed to the highest office of the old church, and before he died he became a bishop.

During the first years after his return from the dreadful wilds the people of the town looked up to him as a man to whom they were bound to do honor and reverence; but they often, also, looked up to the sky to see if there were any signs of the Griffin coming back. However, in course of time, they learned to honor and reverence their former Minor Canon without the fear of being punished if they did not do so.

But they need never have been afraid of the Griffin. The autumnal equinox day came around, and the monster ate nothing. If he could not have the Minor Canon, he did not care for anything. So, lying down, with his eyes fixed upon the great stone griffin, he gradually declined and died. It was a good thing for some of the people of the town that they did not know this.

If you should ever visit the old town, you would still see the little griffins on the sides of the church; but the great stone griffin that was over the door is gone.

"The time has come," the Walrus said,
    "To talk of many things:
Of shoes—and ships—and sealing-wax—
    Of cabbages—and kings."
        From "Through the Looking-Glass." Lewis Carroll.

WILLIAM TELL

By Sheridan Knowles

Legend says that William Tell, one of Switzerland's heroes in its struggle against Austria for independence, had refused to salute the cap which Gessler, the Austrian governor, had hung up in the market-place at Altdorf for that purpose. In punishment he was ordered to shoot an apple off the head of his own son, Albert.

Enter, slowly, Citizens and Women, Gessler, Tell, Albert and Soldiers—one bearing Tell's bow and quiver, another a basket of apples.

Gessler.   That is your ground.   Now shall they measure thence
A hundred paces.   Take the distance.

Tell.   Is the line a true one?

Gessler.   True or not, what is't to thee?

Tell.   What is't to me?   A little thing,
A very little thing—a yard or two
Is nothing here or there—were it a wolf
I shot at!   Never mind.

Gessler.   Be thankful, slave,
Our grace accords thee life on any terms.

Tell.   I will be thankful, Gessler!—Villain, stop!
You measure to the sun!

Gessler.   And what of that?
What matter whether to or from the sun?

Tell.   I'd have it at my back.—The sun should shine

Upon the mark, and not on him that shoots.
I can not see to shoot against the sun—
I will not shoot against the sun!

    Gessler. Give him his way! Thou hast cause to bless
    my mercy.

    Tell. I shall remember it. I'd like to see
The apple I'm to shoot at.

    Gessler. Stay! Show me the basket!—There—

    Tell. You've picked the smallest one.

    Gessler. I know I have.

    Tell. O! do you? But you see
The color on't is dark—I'd have it light,
To see it better.

    Gessler. Take it as it is!
Thy skill will be the greater if thou hit'st it!

    Tell. True—true! I did not think of that—
I wonder I did not think of that.
Give me some chance to save my boy!

            (*Throws away the apple with all his force.*)
I will not murder him,
If I can help it—for the honor of
The form thou wearest, if all the heart is gone.

    Gessler. Well, choose thyself.

    Tell. Have I a friend among the lookers-on?

    Verner. (*Rushing forward.*) Here, Tell!

    Tell. I thank thee, Verner!
He is a friend runs out into a storm
To shake a hand with us. I must be brief;

THE STATUE OF WILLIAM TELL AT ALTDORF

When once the bow is bent, we can not take
The shot too soon.   Verner, whatever be
The issue of this hour, the common cause
Must not stand still.   Let not to-morrow's sun
Set on the tyrant's banner!   Verner! Verner!
The boy!—the boy!   Think'st thou he hath the courage
To stand it?

    Verner.   Yes.

    Tell.   How looks he?

    Verner.   Clear and smilingly.
If you doubt it—look yourself.

    Tell.   No, no! my friend!
To hear it is enough.

    Verner.   He bears himself so much above his years—

    Tell.   I know!—I know!

    Verner.   With constancy so modest!—

    Tell.   I was sure he would—

    Verner.   And looks with such relying love
And reverence upon you—

    Tell.   Man! Man! Man!
No more!   Already I'm too much the father
To act the man!—Verner, no more, my friend!
I would be flint—flint—flint.   Don't make me feel
I'm not—you do not mind me!—Take the boy
And set him, Verner, with his back to me.
Set him upon his knees—and place this apple
Upon his head, so that the stem may front me,—

Thus, Verner; charge him to keep steady—tell him
I'll hit the apple!   Verner, do all this
More briefly than I tell it thee.

Verner.   Come, Albert!   (*Leading him out.*)

Albert.   May I not speak with him before I go?

Verner.   No.

Albert.   I would only kiss his hand.

Verner.   You must not.

Albert.   I must!—I can not go from him without.

Verner.   It is his will you should.

Albert.   His will, is it?

I am content, then—come.

Tell.   If thou canst bear it, should not I?—Go now,
My son—and keep in mind that I can shoot—
Go, boy—be thou steady, I will hit
The apple—Go!—God bless thee—go.—My bow!—
                    (*The bow is handed to him.*)

Thou wilt not fail thy master, wilt thou?—Thou
Hast never failed him yet, old servant—No,
I'm sure of thee—I know thy honesty.
Thou art stanch—stanch.—Let me see my quiver.

Gessler.   Give him a single arrow.

Tell.   Do you shoot?

Soldier.   I do.

Tell.   Is it so you pick an arrow, friend?

The point, you see, is bent; the feather jagged;
                    (*Breaks it.*)

That's all the use 'tis fit for.

Gessler. Let him have another.

Tell. Why, 'tis better than the first,
But yet not good enough for such an aim
As I'm to take—'tis heavy in the shaft:
I'll not shoot with it! (*Throws it away.*) Let me see
   my quiver.
Bring it!—'Tis not one arrow in a dozen
I'd take to shoot with at a dove, much less
A dove like that.—

Gessler. It matters not.
Show him the quiver.

Tell. See if the boy is ready.

Verner. He is.

Tell. I'm ready, too! Keep silence, for
Heaven's sake, and do not stir—and let me have
Your prayers—your prayers—and be my witnesses
That if his life's in peril from my hand
'Tis only for the chance of saving it.

      (*To the people.*)
Now, friends, for mercy's sake, keep motionless
And silent.

 (*Tell shoots, and a shout of exultation bursts from
  the crowd. Tell's head drops on his bosom; he
  with difficulty supports himself upon his bow.*)

 Verner. (*Rushing in with Albert.*) The boy is safe,
 —no hair of him is touched.

Albert.   Father, I'm safe!—your Albert's safe.   Dear
father,—

Speak to me!   Speak to me!

Verner.   He can not, boy!

Albert.   You grant him life?

Gessler.   I do.

Albert.   And we are free?

Gessler.   You are.

Albert.   Thank Heaven!—thank Heaven!

Verner.   Open his coat, and give him air.

   (*Albert opens his father's coat, and an arrow drops.
   Tell starts, fixes his eye upon Albert, and clasps
   him to his breast.*)

Tell.   My boy!—my boy!

Gessler.   For what
Hid you that arrow in your breast?   Speak, slave!

Tell.   To kill thee, tyrant, had I slain my boy?

Abridged.

With malice toward none; with charity for all; with
firmness in the right, as God gives us to see the right, let
us strive on to finish the work we are in; to bind up the
nation's wounds; to care for him who shall have borne
the battle, and for his widow, and his orphan—to do all
which may achieve and cherish a just and lasting peace
among ourselves, and with all nations.

—*From the Second Inaugural Address of Abraham Lincoln.*

JOHNNY DARTER

By David Starr Jordan

David Starr Jordan, one of the greatest scientists in America, was born in Gainesville, New York, in 1851. He was a pupil of Agassiz, the famous naturalist. He served on the United States Fish Commission for fourteen years, was professor of zoölogy at Indiana University, and later president there, and in 1891 was made president of Leland Stanford Junior University, in Palo Alto, California.

Any one who has ever been a boy and can remember back to the days of tag-alders, yellow cowslips, and an angleworm on a pin-hook, will recall an experience like this: You tried some time to put your finger on a little fish that was lying, apparently asleep, on the bottom of the stream, half hidden under a stone or a leaf, his tail bent around the stone as if for support against the force of the current. You will remember that when your finger came near the spot where he was lying, the bent tail was straightened, and you saw the fish again resting, head up-stream, a few feet away, leaving you puzzled to know whether you had seen the movement or not. You were trying to catch a Johnny Darter. Nothing seems easier, but you did not do it.

In all clear streams from Maine to Mexico the Johnny Darters are found; and the boy who does not know them has missed one of the real pleasures of a boy's life. All

of them are very little fishes,—some not more than two
inches long, and the very largest but six or eight.   But
small though they are, they are the most interesting in
habits, the most graceful in form, and many of them the
most brilliant in color of all fresh-water fishes.   The
books call them "Darters," for one of the first species
known was named in Greek "dart body,"—a name most
appropriate to them all.   The boys call them "Johnnies."
Certainly the boys ought to know,—and Johnnies they
are, and Darters they are; so Johnny Darters they shall be.

Rafinesque said of the Johnnies that he knew "they are
good to eat fried."   I suppose that he had tried them; but
we have not.   We should as soon think of filling our pan
with wood warblers as to make a meal of them.   The
good man goes a-fishing, not for "pot-luck," but to let
escape "the Indian within him."

The Johnny Darter deserves our especial attention, for
he is altogether an American product.   He has all that
ardent desire for perfect freedom that is supposed to be
native to this continent.   Unless all appearance of captivity be concealed in a well-kept aquarium, he will
quickly lie on the bottom, dead.   If our tank be so ar-
ranged that the conditions are nearly natural, there being
an abundance of stones and weeds on the bottom, our
Johnnies will cheerfully live with us, and we shall be
ready to study their individual peculiarities.

For it must be known that while all fish are fish, they

are so only as all men are men. The children of one family are not more unlike one another than the fishes of one brook might be if the sickly ones and the lazy ones were as carefully guarded as are ours. One is constantly darting over and among the stones, never resting, moving his head from side to side when his body is for a moment still. Another will lie for hours motionless under a stone, moving only for a few inches when pushed out with a stick.

But we must tell the story of the Johnny Darters that live in the aquarium. All the species here mentioned, and some others, are well known.

First of these in size, and therefore in dignity, comes the Log Perch or Hog-fish. This is the giant of the family,—the most of a fish, and therefore the least of a darter. It may be readily known by its zebra-like colors. Its hue is pale olive,—silvery below, darker above. On this ground-color are about fifteen black vertical bars or incomplete rings, alternating with as many shorter bars which reach only half-way down the side. The hindmost bar forms a mere spot on the base of the tail, and there are many dots and speckles on the fins. The body is long and slender, spindle-shaped, and firm and wiry to the touch. The head is flat on top, and tapers into a flat-pointed snout which is squared off at the end like the snout of a pig.

We next come to the fine gentleman of the family, the

Black-sided Darter. This one we may know by its colors. The ground hue is a salmon yellow; the back is regularly and beautifully marbled with black in a peculiar and handsome pattern. On the sides, from the head to the tail, runs a jet-black band, which is widened at intervals into rounded spots; or we may say that on each side is a chain of round black blotches. Sometimes the fishes seem to fade out; these blotches grow pale, and no longer meet; but in an instant they may regain their original form and shade. This latter change can be induced by the offer of food, and it is, of course, due to muscular action on the scales which cover the darker pigment.

One of the most simply beautiful of all fishes is the Green-sided Darter. He has the beauty of green grass, wild violets, and mossy logs. As we watch him in the water, with his bright blended colors and gentle ways, once more, with Old Izaak, "we sit on cowslip banks, hear the birds sing, and possess ourselves in as much quietness as the silent silver streams which we see glide so quietly by us." During the ordinary business of the year he, like most sensible fishes and men, dresses plainly. But when the first bluebirds give warning by their shivering and bodiless notes that spring is coming, then he puts on his wedding-clothes, and becomes in fact the Green-sided Darter.

Gayest of all the darters, and indeed the gaudiest of all fresh-water fishes, is the Rainbow Darter. This is a little fish, never more than three inches long, and usually about two. Everywhere, throughout the northern parts of the Mississippi Valley, it makes its home in the ripples and shallows of the rivers and in the shady retreats of all the little brooks. The male fish is greenish above, with darker blotches, and its sides are variegated with oblique bands alternately of indigo-blue and deep orange.

When the Civil War broke out, there were some good people who were anxiously looking for a sign or omen, that they might know on which side the "stars in their courses" were fighting. It so happened that in a little brook in Indiana, called Clear Creek, some one caught a Rainbow Darter. This fish was clothed in a new suit of the red, white, and blue of his native land, in the most unmistakably patriotic fashion. There were some people who had never seen a darter before, and who knew no more of the fishes in their streams than these fishes knew of them, by whom the coming of this little "soldier-fish" into their brooks was hailed as an omen of victory. Of course, these little fishes had really always been there. They were there when America was discovered and for a long time before, but the people had not seen them. When the day comes when history shall finally recount all the influences which held Indiana to her place in the Union, shall not, among greater things, this least of little fishes receive its little meed of praise?

From "Science Sketches." Adapted.

SNOW–BOUND

By John Greenleaf Whittier

Circumstances caused Whittier to live a quieter and simpler life than that of any other New England writer. Poverty, ill health, and the plain dress and speech of the Friends, all set him apart from the world. Hard work on his father's farm, bitter cold and scant education marked his youth. One night when he was fourteen the teacher of the neighboring school, who was boarding in the family, read aloud from Burns's poems. The boy was entranced. The teacher kindly left him the book and he pored over it. From that hour he knew himself a poet. His first printed verses were secretly sent by his sister Mary to

the *Newburyport Free Press.* Whittier was working in the field with his father when the paper was handed to him. The editor, who was William Lloyd Garrison, himself then young and obscure, called on the family and urged that so gifted a writer be sent to an academy. At first this seemed impossible, but Whittier himself finally earned enough money by making slippers. When he finished his school year he had just twenty-five cents left. Most of his life was spent in the Whittier homestead at East Haverhill, Massachusetts, or in his later homes at Amesbury and Oak Knoll, Danvers, and he never traveled except to Boston, New York or Philadelphia. Yet he took always the keenest interest in public problems, especially in the problem of slavery. When talking on this subject his large, deep-set eyes—the eyes inherited also by Hawthorne and

Webster from a common ancestor—glowed with indignation. His
poems on the sufferings of slaves stirred the entire country. He
did much to establish schools for freedmen. Once he was stoned
by a mob because of his sympathy with slaves. For many years
Whittier was so ill that he could not work for more than half an
hour at a time. He depended greatly on the love and companion-
ship of his sister Elizabeth and after her death he was very lonely.
But other friends did all they could to make up her loss. To one
of them, while away on a visit, he wrote, "What with the child, and
the dogs, and Rip Van Winkle the cat, and a tame gray squirrel,
who hunts our pockets for nuts, we contrive to get through the
short dark days." Despite his ill health Whittier lived to be eighty-
four. After his death the old house in East Haverhill, where he
was born, was bought by his friends, and its chief room restored as
it was in his boyhood. *Snow-Bound* pictures scenes from his own
home-life.

> We looked upon a world unknown,
> On nothing we could call our own.
> Around the glistening wonder bent
> The blue walls of the firmament,
> No cloud above, no earth below,—
> A universe of sky and snow!
> The old familiar sights of ours
> Took marvelous shapes; strange domes and towers
> Rose up where sty or corn-crib stood,
> Or garden-wall, or belt of wood;
> A smooth white mound the brush-pile showed,
> A fenceless drift what once was road;
> The bridle-post an old man sat
> With loose-flung coat and high cocked hat;

The well-curb had a Chinese roof;
And even the long sweep, high aloof,
In its slant splendor, seemed to tell
Of Pisa's leaning miracle.

Our buskins on our feet we drew;
With mittened hands, and caps drawn low,
To guard our necks and ears from snow,
We cut the solid whiteness through.
And, where the drift was deepest, made
A tunnel walled and overlaid
With dazzling crystal: we had read
Of rare Aladdin's wondrous cave,
And to our own his name we gave.

As night drew on, and, from the crest
Of wooded knolls that ridged the west,
The sun, a snow-blown traveler, sank
From sight beneath the smothering bank,
We piled, with care, our nightly stack
Of wood against the chimney-back,—
The oaken log, green, huge, and thick,
And on its top the stout back-stick,
The knotty fore-stick laid apart,
And filled between with curious art
The ragged brush; then, hovering near,
We watched the first red blaze appear,
Heard the sharp crackle, caught the gleam

On whitewashed wall and sagging beam,
Until the old, rude-furnished room
Burst, flower-like, into rosy bloom;
While radiant with a mimic flame
Outside the sparkling drift became,
And through the bare-boughed lilac-tree
Our own warm hearth seemed blazing free.
The crane and pendent trammels showed,
The Turks' heads on the andirons glowed;
While childish fancy, prompt to tell
The meaning of the miracle,
Whispered the old rhyme: "*Under the tree,*
When fire outdoors burns merrily,
There the witches are making tea."

The moon above the eastern wood
Shone at its full; the hill-range stood
Transfigured in the silver flood,
Its blown snows flashing cold and keen,
Dead white, save where some sharp ravine
Took shadow, or the somber green
Of hemlocks turned to pitchy black
Against the whiteness at their back.
For such a world and such a night
Most fitting that unwarming light,
Which only seemed where'er it fell
To make the coldness visible.

Shut in from all the world without,
We sat the clean-winged hearth about,
Content to let the north-wind roar
In baffled rage at pane and door,
While the red logs before us beat
The frost-line back with tropic heat;
And ever, when a louder blast
Shook beam and rafter as it passed,
The merrier up its roaring draught
The great throat of the chimney laughed;
The house-dog on his paws outspread
Laid to the fire his drowsy head,
The cat's dark silhouette on the wall
A couchant tiger's seemed to fall;
And, for the winter fireside meet,
Between the andirons' straddling feet,
The mug of cider simmered slow,
The apples sputtered in a row,
And, close at hand, the basket stood
With nuts from brown October's wood.

What matter how the night behaved?
What matter how the north-wind raved?
Blow high, blow low, not all its snow
Could quench our hearth-fire's ruddy glow.

Abridged.

A LETTER TO HIS SISTER

By Felix Mendelssohn

Jakob Ludwig Felix Mendelssohn, one of the world's great musicians, was born in Hamburg, Germany, on the third of February,

1809. His grandfather had been known as the most accomplished scholar in Europe. His mother was a brilliant woman, with unusual talent in music. Felix had two sisters and one brother. His sister Fanny, who was four years his elder, was his closest and dearest companion The mother began piano lessons with Fanny and Felix when the former was seven and the latter but three years old. Their first lessons were only five minutes long. Gradually the time lengthened, however, until the children began to practise at five o'clock in the morning. They worked practically all day, every day in the week except Sunday. When they had advanced too far for their mother's instruction they were placed under the best teacher in Germany. At fifteen Mendelssohn was a celebrated musician. During all of these years his love for his sister Fanny continued. They read together Shakespeare's *Midsummer Night's Dream* which had just been translated into German. Mendelssohn was so impressed by its beauty that he was inspired to compose music to the drama. He and Fanny kept the matter a secret until the work was done, and then they played it as a piano duet, a surprise for their friends. Mendelssohn was one of the most delightful of letter writers. He died in 1847.

WEIMAR, November 8, 1821.

DEAREST FANNY:

To-day is Thursday. On Sunday the son of Weimar, Goethe, arrived. We went to church in the morning and heard half of Handel's Music to the One Hundredth Psalm. After church I wrote that little letter dated the fourth inst. and went to the Elephant Hotel where I made a sketch. Two hours later Professor Zelter came, calling out, "Goethe has come, the old gentleman has come!" We instantly hurried down-stairs and went to Goethe's house. He was in the garden, just coming round a hedge. He is very kindly, but I do not think any of his portraits look like him. He does not look like a man of seventy-three, rather like one of fifty.

In the afternoon I played to Goethe for about two hours, partly fugues of Bach and partly improvisation. Yesterday morning I took your songs to Frau von Goethe, who has a good voice and will sing them to the old gentleman. I told him that you had written them and asked him whether he would like to hear them. He said, "Yes, yes, with pleasure." Frau von Goethe likes them very much.

On Thursday morning the Grand Duke and Duchess came to us and I had to play. I played from eleven in the morning till ten in the evening, with only two hours' interruption. Every afternoon Goethe opens his instrument with these words, "I have not heard you to-day— now make a little noise for me." And then he generally sits down by my side and when I have done (mostly extemporizing) I ask for a kiss or take one. You can not fancy how good and kind he is to me.

Always your loving,

FELIX.

From " Letters of Felix Mendelssohn." Adapted.

THE SOUTH WIND AND THE SUN

BY JAMES WHITCOMB RILEY

O the South Wind and the Sun!
How each loved the other one—
Full of fancy—full of folly—
Full of jollity and fun!
How they romped and ran about,
Like two boys when school is out,
With glowing face, and lisping lip,
Low laugh, and lifted shout!

And the South Wind—he was dressed
With a ribbon round his breast
That floated, flapped and fluttered
In a riotous unrest;
And a drapery of mist,
From the shoulder and the wrist
Flowing backward with the motion
Of the waving hand he kissed.

And the Sun had on a crown
Wrought of gilded thistle-down,
And a scarf of velvet vapor,
And a raveled-rainbow gown;
And his tinsel-tangled hair,
Tossed and lost upon the air,
Was glossier and flossier
Than any anywhere.

And the South Wind's eyes were two
Little dancing drops of dew,
As he puffed his cheeks, and pursed his lips,
And blew and blew and blew!
And the Sun's—like diamond-stone—
Brighter yet than ever known,
As he knit his brows and held his breath,
And shone and shone and shone!

And this pair of merry fays
Wandered through the summer days;
Arm-in-arm they went together
Over heights of morning haze—
Over slanting slopes of lawn
They went on and on and on,
Where the daisies looked like star-tracks
Trailing up and down the dawn.

Abridged.

DAN AND UNA

By Rudyard Kipling

In 1878 there was placed at Westward Ho College, Northam, England, a small boy who was to spend his next five years there

while his father and mother were far away in India. This boy was Rudyard Kipling, named from the English lake beside which his father and mother had first met. He had been born, thirteen years before, in Bombay, "between the palms and the sea," where his father, a gifted artist, taught in the English government School of Art. While at Westward Ho Kipling edited, for two years, the school paper, and from time to time he wrote clever little sketches and verses for it. When he went back home to India, he took with him the first prize in English literature. He had made up his mind to write, and entered a newspaper office in Lahore as a reporter. During his service there Kipling came to know picturesque India as no one else had known it. By his side in the office dark-skinned natives worked setting up type. He explored the jungles, learning the ways of elephant, wolf and jaguar, and he went from one army post to another, making fast friends with "Tommy Atkins," as the British private soldier is called. Ballads and stories of this life appeared first in the paper for which he worked, and afterwards in book form. For a time no publisher could be found either in America or in England, but when his work finally came out in London he was instantly famous. Andrew Lang hailed him as "a new star in the East."

Few writers have interested such widely different people. Once when Kipling was on a steamer entering New York harbor, a strange pilot in a tug, to whom he had been pointed out on deck, snatched off his oil skin cap and shouted out across the rough sea some stirring sailor lines. For a moment Kipling stood astonished, —the lines were his own. Then he too took off his cap and waved a hearty salute, as to a comrade. After fame had come to him he went back to India and visited the old newspaper office at Lahore. As soon as he appeared in the door the Mohammedan foreman flew about, his green turban awry, telling all hands with delight that "Kuppuleen Sahib" (Lord Kipling) had come back. Kipling married an American woman and lived for a time in Vermont. He lives now in England in a charming old farm-house which he has altered to suit his needs. What a delightful home it must be where the father can write for his children such fascinating stories! Kipling is very reserved, very busy, very much in earnest. Children love his *Jungle Books*, his *Captains Courageous*, his *Just So Stories*, and his *Puck of Pook's Hill*, from the first chapter of which the story following is taken.

The children were at the theater, acting to Three Cows as much as they could remember of *Midsummer Night's Dream*. Their father had made them a small play out of the big Shakespeare one, and they had rehearsed it with him and with their mother till they could say it by heart. They began where Nick Bottom, the weaver, comes out of the bushes with a donkey's head on his shoulders, and finds Titania, Queen of the Fairies, asleep. Then they skipped to the part where Bottom asks three little fairies to scratch his head and bring him honey, and they ended where he falls asleep in Titania's arms. Dan was Puck and Nick Bottom, as well as all the three fairies. He wore a pointy-eared cloth cap for Puck, and a paper donkey's head out of a Christmas cracker—but it tore if you were not careful—for Bottom. Una was Titania, with a wreath of columbines and a foxglove wand.

The theater lay in a meadow called the Long Slip. A little mill-stream, carrying water to a mill two or three fields away, bent round one corner of it, and in the middle of the bend lay a large old fairy Ring of darkened grass, which was their stage. The mill-stream banks, overgrown with willow, hazel, and guelder rose, made convenient places to wait in till your turn came; and a grown-up who had seen it said that Shakespeare himself could not have imagined a more suitable setting for his play. They were not, of course, allowed to act on Midsummer Night itself, but they went down after tea on Midsummer Eve, when the shadows were growing, and they took their supper— hard-boiled eggs, biscuits, and salt in an envelope—with them. Three Cows had been milked and were grazing steadily with a tearing noise that one could hear all down the meadow; and the noise of the mill at work sounded like bare feet running on hard ground. A cuckoo sat on a gate-post singing his broken June tune, "cuckoo-cuk," while a busy kingfisher crossed from the mill-stream to the brook which ran on the other side of the meadow. Everything else was a sort of thick, sleepy stillness, smelling of meadow-sweet and dry grass.

Their play went beautifully.   Dan remembered all his parts—Puck, Bottom, and all the three fairies—and Una never forgot a word of Titania—not even the difficult piece where she tells the fairies how to feed Bottom with "apricocks, ripe figs, and dewberries," and all the lines end in "ies."   They were both so pleased that they acted it three times over from beginning to end before they sat down in the unthistly center of the Ring to eat eggs and biscuits.   This was when they heard a whistle among the alders on the bank, and they jumped.

The bushes parted.   In the very spot where Dan had stood as Puck they saw a small, brown, broad-shouldered, pointy-eared person with a snub nose, slanting blue eyes, and a grin that ran right across his freckled face.   He shaded his forehead as though he were watching Quince, Snout, Bottom and the others rehearsing Pyramus and Thisbe, and, in a voice as deep as Three Cows asking to be milked, he began:

"What hempen home-spuns have we swaggering here,
    So near the cradle of the fairy queen?"

He stopped, hollowed one hand round his ear, and with a wicked twinkle in his eye, went on:

" What, a play toward?   I'll be an auditor;
    An actor too perhaps, if I see cause."

The children looked and gasped.   The small thing—he

was no taller than Dan's shoulder—stepped quietly into the Ring.

"I'm rather out of practice," said he; "but that's the way my part ought to be played."

Still the children stared at him—from his dark-blue cap, like a big columbine flower, to his bare, hairy feet. At last he laughed.

"Please don't look like that. It isn't my fault. What else could you expect?" he said.

"We didn't expect any one," Dan answered slowly. "This is our field."

"Is it?" said their visitor, sitting down. "Then what on Human Earth made you act *Midsummer Night's Dream* three times over, on Midsummer Eve, in the middle of a Ring, and under—right under one of my oldest hills in old England? Pook's Hill—Puck's Hill—Puck's Hill—Pook's Hill! It's as plain as the nose on my face!"

He pointed to the bare, fern-covered slope of Pook's Hill that runs up from the far side of the mill-stream to a dark wood. Beyond that wood the ground rises and rises for five hundred feet, till at last you climb out on the bare top of Beacon Hill, to look over the Pevensey Levels and the Channel and half the naked South Downs.

"By Oak, Ash and Thorn!" he cried, still laughing. "If this had happened a few hundred years ago you'd have had all the people of the hills out like bees in June!"

"We didn't know it was wrong," said Dan.

A POINTY-EARED PERSON WITH A SNUB NOSE

"Wrong!" The little fellow shook with laughter. "Indeed it isn't wrong. You've done something that Kings and Knights and Scholars in old days would have given their crowns and spurs and books to find out. If Merlin himself had helped you, you couldn't have managed better! You've broken the Hills! You've broken the Hills! It hasn't happened in a thousand years."

"We—we didn't mean to," said Una.

"Of course you didn't! That's just why you did it! Unluckily the Hills are empty now, and all the People of the Hills are gone. I'm the only one left. I'm Puck, the oldest Old Thing in England, very much at your service if you care to have anything to do with me. If you don't, of course you've only to say so, and I'll go."

He looked at the children and the children looked at him for quite half a minute. His eyes did not twinkle any more. They were very kind, and there was the beginning of a good smile on his lips.

Una put out her hand. "Don't go," she said. "We like you!"

"Have a biscuit," said Dan, and he passed over the squashy envelope with the eggs.

"By Oak, Ash and Thorn!" cried Puck, taking off his blue cap, "I like you, too. Sprinkle a little salt on the biscuit, Dan, and I'll eat it with you. That'll show you the sort of person I am. Some of us," he went on,— with his mouth full—"couldn't abide Salt, or Horseshoes over a door, or Mountain-ash berries, or Running Water, or Cold Iron, or the sound of Church Bells. But I'm Puck!"

He brushed the crumbs carefully from his doublet and shook hands.

"We always said, Dan and I," Una stammered, "that if it ever happened we'd know ex-actly what to do; but— but now it seems all different somehow."

"She means meeting a fairy," said Dan. "I never believed in 'em—not after I was six, anyhow."

"Aren't you most awfully old?" said Una.

"Not old—fairly long-lived, as folks say hereabouts. Let me see—my friends used to set my dish of cream for me o' nights when Stonehenge was new."

Una clasped her hands, cried, "Oh!" and nodded her head.

"I was thinking—suppose we saved some of our porridge and put it in the attic for you," she said.

"Bless your heart o' gold!" said Puck. "You'll make a fine considering wench some market-day. I really don't want you to put out a bowl for me; but if ever I need a bite, be sure I'll tell you."

Puck stretched himself at length on the dry grass, and the children stretched out beside him, their bare legs waving happily in the air. They felt they could not be afraid of him any more than of their particular friend, old Hobden, the hedger. He did not bother them with grown-up questions, or laugh at the donkey's head, but lay and smiled to himself in the most sensible way.

"Have you a knife on you?" he said at last.

Dan handed over his big one-bladed outdoor knife, and Puck began to carve out a piece of turf from the center of the Ring.

"What's that for—Magic?" said Una, as he pressed up the square of chocolate loam that cut like so much cheese.

"One of my little Magics," he answered, and cut another. "You see, I can't let you into the Hills because the People of the Hills have gone; but if you care to take seizin from me, I may be able to show you something out of the common here on Human Earth. You certainly deserve it."

"What's taking seizin?" said Dan cautiously.

"It's an old custom the people had when they bought and sold land. They used to cut out a clod and hand it over to the buyer, and you weren't lawfully seized of your land—it didn't really belong to you—till the other fellow had actually given you a piece of it—like this." He held out the turfs.

"But it's our own meadow," said Dan, drawing back. "Are you going to magic it away?"

Puck laughed. "I know it's your meadow, but there's a great deal more in it than you or your father ever guessed. Try!"

He turned his eyes on Una.

"I'll do it," she said. Dan followed her example at once.

"Now are you two lawfully seized and possessed of all Old England," began Puck, in a sing-song voice. "By Right of Oak, Ash, and Thorn, are you free to come and go and look and know where I shall show or best you please. You shall see What you shall see and you shall hear What you shall hear, though It shall have happened three thousand year; and you shall know neither Doubt nor Fear. Fast! Hold fast all I give you."

The children shut their eyes, but nothing happened.

"Well?" said Una, disappointedly opening them. "I thought there would be dragons."

"Though It shall have happened three thousand year," said Puck, and counted on his fingers. "No; I'm afraid there were no dragons three thousand years ago."

"But there hasn't happened anything at all," said Dan.

"Wait a while," said Puck. "You don't grow an oak in a year—and Old England's older than twenty oaks. Let's sit down again and think. *I* can do that for a century at a time."

.   .   .   .

"Just now it seems to me that, unless you go back to the house, people will be looking for you. I'll walk with you as far as the gate."

"Will you be here when we come again?" they asked.

"Surely, sure-ly," said Puck. "I've been here some time already. One minute first, please."

He gave them each three leaves—one of Oak, one of Ash, and one of Thorn.

"Bite these," said he. "Otherwise you might be talking at home of what you've seen and heard, and —if I know human beings—they'd send for the doctor. Bite!"

They bit hard, and found themselves walking side by side to the lower gate. Their father was leaning over it.

"And how did your play go?" he asked.

"Oh, splendidly," said Dan. "Only afterwards, I think, we went to sleep. It was very hot and quiet. Don't you remember, Una?"

Una shook her head and said nothing.

"I see," said her father.

> "'Late—late in the evening Kilmeny came home,
> For Kilmeny had been she could not tell where,
> And Kilmeny had seen what she could not declare.'

"But why are you chewing leaves at your time of life, daughter? For fun?"

"No. It was for something, but I can't azactly remember," said Una.

From "Puck of Pook's Hill."

TITANIA AND OBERON

FAIRY SCENES FROM A MIDSUMMER NIGHT'S DREAM

BY WILLIAM SHAKESPEARE

ACT II

SCENE I.   A wood near Athens

(Enter, from opposite sides, a Fairy and Puck.)

Puck.   How now, spirit! whither wander you?
Fairy.   Over hill, over dale,
  Thorough bush, thorough brier,
Over park, over pale,
  Thorough flood, thorough fire,
I do wander every where,
Swifter than the moon's sphere;
And I serve the fairy queen,
To dew her orbs upon the green.
The cowslips tall her pensioners be.
In their gold coats spots you see;
Those be rubies, fairy favors,
In those freckles live their savors.
I must go seek some dewdrops here,
And hang a pearl in every cowslip's ear.
Farewell, thou lob of spirits; I'll be gone;
Our queen and all her elves come here anon.
Puck.   The king doth keep his revels here
  to-night:
Take heed the queen come not within his sight;

For Oberon is passing fell and wrath,
Because that she as her attendant hath
A lovely boy, stolen from an Indian king.
She never had so sweet a changeling;
And jealous Oberon would have the child
Knight of his train, to trace the forests wild.
But she perforce withholds the loved boy,
Crowns him with flowers and makes him all her
    joy:
And now they never meet in grove or green,
By fountain clear, or spangled starlight sheen,
But they do square, that all their elves for fear
Creep into acorn-cups and hide them there.

Fairy. Either I mistake your shape and making
    quite,
Or else you are that shrewd and knavish sprite
Call'd Robin Goodfellow. Are not you he
That frights the maidens of the villagery;
Skim milk, and sometimes labor in the quern,
And bootless make the breathless housewife churn;
And sometime make the drink to bear no barm;
Mislead night-wanderers, laughing at their harm?
Those that Hobgoblin call you and sweet Puck,
You do their work, and they shall have good luck.
Are not you he?

Puck. Thou speak'st aright;
I am that merry wanderer of the night.

I jest to Oberon, and make him smile,
When I a fat and bean-fed horse beguile,
Neighing in likeness of a filly foal;
And sometime lurk I in a gossip's bowl,
In very likeness of a roasted crab;
And when she drinks, against her lips I bob
And on her wither'd dewlap pour the ale.
The wisest aunt, telling the saddest tale,
Sometime for three-foot stool mistaketh me;
Then slip I from her, then down topples she,
And " tailor " cries, and falls into a cough;
And then the whole choir hold their hips and laugh,
And waxen in their mirth, and neeze, and swear
A merrier hour was never wasted there.
But, room, fairy! here comes Oberon.

Fairy.   And here my mistress.   Would that he
          were gone!

(*Enter, from one side, Oberon with his train; from
the other Titania with hers.   They quarrel about the
child, whom Titania refuses to surrender.   In a pout she
leaves the scene, followed by her attendants.*)

Oberon.   My gentle Puck, come hither.
          Fetch me that flower; the herb I show'd thee once.
          The juice of it on sleeping eyelids laid
          Will make or man or woman madly dote
          Upon the next live creature that it sees.

Fetch me this herb, and be thou here again
Ere the leviathan can swim a league.

Puck. I'll put a girdle round about the earth in forty
minutes. *(Exit.)*

Oberon. Having once this juice,
I'll watch Titania when she is asleep,
And drop the liquor of it in her eyes.
The next thing then she waking looks upon,
Be it on lion, bear, or wolf, or bull,
On meddling monkey, or on busy ape,
She shall pursue it with the soul of love;
And ere I take this charm from off her sight,
As I can take it with another herb,
I'll make her render up her page to me. *(Reёnter Puck.)*
Hast thou the flower there? Welcome, wanderer.

Puck. Aye, there it is.

Oberon. I pray thee, give it me.
I know a bank where the wild thyme blows,
Where oxlips and the nodding violet grows;
Quite over-canopied with luscious woodbine,
With sweet musk-roses, and with eglantine.
There sleeps Titania sometime of the night,
Lull'd in these flowers with dances and delight;
And there the snake throws her enamell'd skin,
Weed wide enough to wrap a fairy in;
And with the juice of this I'll streak her eyes,
And make her full of hateful fantasies.

SCENE II.   Another part of the wood.

(*Enter Titania, with her train.*)

Titania.   Come, now a roundel and a fairy song;
Then, for the third part of a minute, hence;
Some to kill cankers in the musk-rose buds;
Some war with rere-mice for their leathern wings,
To make my small elves coats; and some keep back
The clamorous owl, that nightly hoots and wonders
At our quaint spirits.   Sing me now asleep;
Then to your offices, and let me rest.

(*The Fairies sing.*)

First Fairy.   You spotted snakes with double tongue,
                    Thorny hedgehogs, be not seen;
                Newts and blind-worms, do no wrong,
                    Come not near our fairy queen.

Chorus.   Philomel, with melody,
                Sing in our sweet lullaby;
            Lulla, lulla, lullaby, lulla, lulla, lullaby.
                    Never harm,
                    Nor spell, nor charm,
                Come our lovely lady nigh;
                So, good night, with lullaby.

Second Fairy.   Weaving spiders, come not here;
        Hence, you long-legged spiders, hence!
    Beetles black, approach not near;
    Worm nor snail, do no offense.

    Chorus.   Philomel, with melody,
        Sing in our sweet lullaby;
Lulla, lulla, lullaby, lulla, lulla, lullaby.
        Never harm,
        Nor spell, nor charm,
    Come our lovely lady nigh;
    So, good night, with lullaby.

  First Fairy.   Hence, away! now all is well;
        One aloof stand sentinel.

      (*Exeunt Fairies. Titania sleeps.*)

  (*Enter Oberon, and squeezes the flower on
          Titania's eyelids.*)

  Oberon. What thou seest when thou dost wake,
Do it for thy true-love take;
Love and languish for his sake:
Be it ounce, or cat, or bear,
Pard, or boar with bristled hair,
In thy eye that shall appear
When thou wak'st, it is thy dear:
Wake when some vile thing is near.   (*Exit.*)

ACT III   SCENE I

In another part of the wood a band of artisans from Athens,
including Bottom, a weaver, Quince, a carpenter, Flute, a bellows-
mender, and Snout, a tinker, are rehearsing a play.

(*Enter Puck behind.*)

Puck.   What hempen homespuns have we swaggering
        here,
So near the cradle of the fairy queen?
What, a play toward! I'll be an auditor;
An actor too perhaps, if I see cause.

Quince.   Speak, Pyramus.—Thisby, stand forth.

Bottom.   Thisby, the flowers of odious savors sweet,—

Quince.   Odors, odors.

Bottom.   —odors savors sweet;
        So hath thy breath, my dearest Thisby dear.
    But hark, a voice! stay thou but here awhile,
        And by and by I will to thee appear.

                                        (*Exit.*)

Puck.   A stranger Pyramus than e'er played here!

                                        (*Exit.*)

Flute.   Must I speak now?

Quince.   Ay, marry, must you; for you must understand he goes but to see a noise that he heard, and is to
come again.

    (*Reënter Puck, and Bottom wearing an ass's head.*)

Bottom. If I were fair, Thisby, I were only thine.

Quince. O monstrous! O strange! we are haunted. Pray, masters! fly, masters! Help!

(*Exeunt Quince, Flute and Snout.*)

Puck. I'll follow you, I'll lead you about a round,
   Through bog, through bush, through brake, through brier:
Sometime a horse I'll be, sometime a hound,
   A hog, a headless bear, sometime a fire;
And neigh, and bark, and grunt, and roar, and burn,
Like horse, hound, hog, bear, fire, at every turn.

(*Exit.*)

Bottom. Why do they run away? this is a knavery of them to make me afeard.

(*Reënter Snout.*)

Snout. O Bottom, thou art changed! what do I see on thee?

Bottom. What do you see? you see an ass-head of your own, do you?

(*Exit Snout.*)

(*Reënter Quince.*)

Quince. Bless thee, Bottom! bless thee! thou art translated.

(*Exit.*)

Bottom. I see their knavery: this is to make an ass of me; to fright me, if they could. But I will not stir from

O MONSTROUS! O STRANGE! WE ARE HAUNTED

this place, do what they can: I will walk up and down here, and I will sing, that they shall hear I am not afraid. (*Sings.*)

  The ousel cock so black of hue,
   With orange-tawny bill,
  The throstle with his note so true,
   The wren with little quill,—

Titania. What angel wakes me from my flowery bed?
Bottom. (*Sings.*)

  The finch, the sparrow, and the lark,
   The plain-song cuckoo gray,
  Whose note full many a man doth mark,
   And dares not answer nay;—

for, indeed, who would set his wit to so foolish a bird? who would give a bird the lie, though he cry "cuckoo" never so?

Titania. I pray thee, gentle mortal, sing again:
 Mine ear is much enamor'd of thy note;
 So is mine eye enthralled to thy shape,
 And thy fair virtue's force perforce doth move me
 On the first view to say, to swear, I love thee.

Bottom. Methinks, mistress, you should have little reason for that: and yet, to say the truth, reason and love keep little company together now-a-days; the more the pity, that some honest neighbors will not make them friends. Nay, I can gleek upon occasion.

Titania. Thou art as wise as thou art beautiful.

Bottom. Not so, neither: but if I had wit enough to get out of this wood, I have enough to serve mine own turn.

Titania. Out of this wood do not desire to go:
Thou shalt remain here, whether thou wilt or no.
I am a spirit of no common rate.
The summer still doth tend upon my state;
And I do love thee; therefore, go with me.
I'll give thee fairies to attend on thee;
And they shall fetch thee jewels from the deep,
And sing, while thou on pressed flowers dost sleep:
And I will purge thy mortal grossness so,
That thou shalt like an airy spirit go.
Peaseblossom! Cobweb! Moth! and Mustardseed!

(*Enter Peaseblossom, Cobweb, Moth, and
Mustardseed.*)

Peaseblossom. Ready.
Cobweb. And I.
Moth. And I.
Mustardseed. And I.
All. Where shall we go?

Titania. Be kind and courteous to this gentleman;
Hop in his walks, and gambol in his eyes;
Feed him with apricocks and dewberries,
With purple grapes, green figs, and mulberries:

The honey-bags steal from the humble-bees,
And for night-tapers crop their waxen thighs,
And light them at the fiery glow-worm's eyes,
To have my love to bed and to arise;
And pluck the wings from painted butterflies
To fan the moonbeams from his sleeping eyes.
Nod to him, elves, and do him courtesies.

Peaseblossom. Hail, mortal!

Cobweb.　　　　　　Hail!

Moth.　　　　　　Hail!

Mustardseed.　　　　　　Hail!

Titania. Come, wait upon him; lead him to my bower.　　　　　　　　　　(*Exeunt.*)

ACT IV　SCENE I

(*Enter Titania and Bottom; Peaseblossom, Cobweb, Moth, Mustardseed, and other Fairies attending; Oberon behind unseen.*)

Titania. Come, sit thee down upon this flowery bed.

Bottom. Where's Peaseblossom?

Peaseblossom. Ready.

Bottom. Scratch my head, Peaseblossom.—Where's Mounsieur Cobweb?

Cobweb. Ready.

Bottom. Mounsieur Cobweb, good mounsieur, get you

your weapons in your hand, and kill me a red-hipped humble-bee on the top of a thistle; and, good mounsieur, bring me the honey-bag. Do not fret yourself too much in the action, mounsieur; and, good mounsieur, have a care the honey-bag break not; I would be loath to have you overflown with a honey-bag, signior. Where's Mounsieur Mustardseed?

Mustardseed. Ready.

Bottom. Give me your neaf, Mounsieur Mustardseed. Pray you, leave your courtesy, good mounsieur.

Mustardseed. What's your will?

Bottom. Nothing, good mounsieur, but to help Cavalery Cobweb to scratch. I must to the barber's, mounsieur, for methinks I am marvelous hairy about the face; and I am such a tender ass, if my hair do but tickle me I must scratch.

Titania. What, wilt thou hear some music, my sweet love?

Bottom. I have a reasonable good ear in music. Let's have the tongs and the bones.

Titania. Or say, sweet love, what thou desir'st to eat.

Bottom. Truly, a peck of provender; I could munch your good dry oats. Methinks I have a great desire to a bottle of hay: good hay, sweet hay, hath no fellow.

Titania. I have a venturous fairy that shall seek the squirrel's hoard, and fetch thee new nuts.

Bottom. I had rather have a handful or two of dried

18—4th

peas. But, I pray you, let none of your people stir me:
I have an exposition of sleep come upon me.

Titania. Sleep thou:
Fairies, be gone, and be all ways away.—

(*Exeunt Fairies.*)

(*Enter Puck.*)

Oberon. (*Advancing*) Welcome, good Robin. See'st
thou this sweet sight?
Her dotage now I do begin to pity;
For, meeting her of late behind the wood,
Seeking sweet favors for this hateful fool,
I did upbraid her and fall out with her:
For she his hairy temples then had rounded
With coronet of fresh and fragrant flowers;
And that same dew, which sometime on the buds
Was wont to swell like round and orient pearls,
Stood now within the pretty flowerets' eyes
Like tears that did their own disgrace bewail.
When I had at my pleasure taunted her
And she in mild terms begg'd my patience,
I then did ask of her her changeling child,
Which straight she gave me, and her fairy sent
To bear him to my bower in fairy land.
And now I have the boy, I will undo
This hateful imperfection of her eyes:
And, gentle Puck, take this transformed scalp

From off the head of this Athenian swain;
That, he awaking   .   .   .
May to Athens back again repair
And think no more of this night's accidents
But as the fierce vexation of a dream.
But first I will release the fairy queen.

> Be as thou wast wont to be,
> See as thou wast wont to see:
> Dian's bud o'er Cupid's flower
> Hath such force and blessed power.

Now, my Titania; wake you, my sweet queen.

Titania.   My Oberon! what visions have I seen!

Puck.   If we shadows have offended,
> Think but this, and all is mended,
> That you have but slumber'd here
> While these visions did appear.
> And this weak and idle theme,
> Gentles, do not reprehend.
> Give me your hands, if we be friends,
> And Robin shall restore amends.

From "A Midsummer Night's Dream." Adapted.

NOTES

When a word has more than one meaning or is used figuratively, the definition given is the one that will aid in the direct interpretation of the text.

TOM, THE CHIMNEY SWEEP

North country, northern part of England; **court,** a space opening from a street and nearly surrounded by houses; **soot** (sŏŏt, or sōōt); **velveteens and ankle-jacks,** cotton velvet breeches and gaiters; **apprentice,** a boy learning a trade, such as Tom himself; **smart,** showily dressed; **groom,** one who takes care of horses; **halloed** (from hăl-lōō); **assure,** declare to; **slag,** bad ore that does not melt in furnaces; **pit-engine,** one used in a coal pit; **sedges,** tall grasses; **madder,** a plant used in dyeing red; **Galway,** a county in Ireland on the sea-coast; **bottle-heath,** a kind of evergreen shrub; **limestone,** a kind of rock, one variety of which is marble; **beadle,** an officer in England who keeps order; **Vendale,** a place where Grimes had committed a crime; **cowed,** depressed with fear; **lime avenue,** an avenue of linden or basswood trees; **tremendous** (three syllables, -dŭs); **altered,** changed; **quality,** people of rank.

THE HOUSE IN BIDWELL STREET

Scantling, boards; **clad,** clothed; **eavesdropping,** listening secretly; why especially a good word here? **uncounted,** of no account; **thoroughfare,** street; **sextette,** a group of six; **reluctant,** unwilling; **critically,** in a fault-finding way; **rafter,** timber in the roof; **exile,** banishment; **tolerated,** put up with; **occasional,** once in a while; **dimensions,** size; **indignant,** angry; **merits,** virtues; **conspicuous,** attracting the eye; **gloom,** darkness; **offend,** displease; **pudgy,** short and fat; **crinkled,** wrinkled; **utterly,** entirely; **pre-**

posterous, foolish; **cutlery,** hardware; **cumbersome,** hard to manage; **service,** use; **promenaded,** walked up and down; **stroke of fortune,** good luck; **droning lullaby,** a sleepy song.

OUT TO OLD AUNT MARY'S

Squat, low; "**red heads,**" woodpeckers; **awry,** to one side; **feign,** pretend; **quest,** desire, end; **minor,** lesser; **fantasy,** "making believe"; "**Out to old Aunt Mary's**", quoted as a refrain.

HOW THEY BROUGHT THE GOOD NEWS FROM GHENT TO AIX

Ghent (gent), capital of a province in Belgium; **Aix** (āks), a city in France; there is no historical foundation for this poem; **askance,** sideways; **spume-flakes,** foam.

LITTLE NELL

Attitude, position; **unconscious of intruders,** did not know any one else was present; **Punch and Judy,** a comical puppet-show; **gallows,** a framework upon which Punch was hanged; **ruefully,** sorrowfully; **diminished,** lessened; **Pan,** god of shepherds, usually represented with the body of a man and the legs of a goat.

THE COCK AND THE FOX

Frugal, scanty; **battlements,** outer walls; **discreet,** prudent; **deigning,** condescending; **high converse,** talk about lofty matters; **destined,** doomed; **treachery,** trickery; **mermaid,** a mythical creature, half woman, half fish; **lustily,** heartily; **lamentation,** wailing; **pursuers,** those running after; **trice,** instant.

THE DIVERTING HISTORY OF JOHN GILPIN

Credit, trusted by people; **renown,** fame; **train-band Captain,** a member of the militia; **repair,** go; **Bell,** an inn; **chaise,** a two-wheeled carriage; **pair,** two horses; why **we,** instead of **us** in fourth stanza? **linen-draper,** a dealer in linen; **calender,** one who glazes cloth or paper; **frugal,** economical; **agog,** eager; **saddletree,** frame of the saddle; **rig,** frolic; **reeking,** perspiring; **accosted,** spoke to.

ICARUS AND DÆDALUS

Crete, an island south of Greece; **Dædalus** (dĕ′-da-lus); **labyrinth,** maze; **veered,** turned; **Icarus** (ik′-a-rus); **winnow,** fan; **cleave,** cut; **fledgling,** a young bird just able to fly; **Apollo,** the sun god; **Cupid,** the god of love; **sustained,** held up; **halcyonbird,** kingfisher, said to lay its eggs on the waves; **vaguely,** dimly

DARIUS GREEN AND HIS FLYING-MACHINE

Aspiring, with high hopes; **genius,** one with unusual gifts or power; **awry** (a-ri′), turned to one side; **riveted,** fastened; **grimace,** a grin of contempt; **dominion,** territory; **pinion,** wing; **azure,** blue; **lurk,** lie hidden; **calked,** filled in; **accoutered** (ăk-kōō′ tered), dressed; **sphere,** place; **abyss,** a bottomless gulf.

CHRISTMAS AT THE CRATCHITS'

Conferred upon, given as an honor; **gallantly,** like a gallant, a fashionable gentleman; **basking,** warming; **luxurious,** rich; **exalted,** praised; **officious zeal,** evident eagerness; **exclusive,** without; **seasonable,** proper for Christmas; **declension,** falling; **rampant,** leaping; **prematurely,** before the proper time; **rallied,** joked; **credulity,** readiness to believe anything told; **tremulous,** trembling; **hob,** a shelf by the grate; **simmer,** boil slowly; **ubiquitous** (ū-bĭk′-wĭ-tŭs), in all places at the same time; **ensued,** followed; **phenomenon,** an unusual event; **incredible,** unbelievable; **succeeded,** followed; **issued,** came; **themes,** subjects; **universal,** all around; **eked,** helped; **surveying,** looking at; **atom,** bit; **steeped,** soaked in; **livid,** gray; **ignited,** lighted; **bedight,** decked.

HORATIUS AT THE BRIDGE

Horatius Cocles (ho-rā'-shi-us kō'-klez); **Tarquinius** (tär-kwin'-i-us); **constant,** unchanging; **Sextus,** son of Tarquinius; **Lars Porsena,** (pôr'-se-nä), his chief helper; **deigning** (dān'-ing), condescending; **craven,** coward; **Palatinus,** one of the seven hills of Rome; **ranks of Tuscany,** soldiers under Porsena; **Comitium** (kō-mish'-ium), a meeting place near the Forum.

MAGGIE VISITS THE GIPSIES

Accordingly, as such; **skewer,** a wooden stick; **placid,** peaceful; **tremor,** trembling; **attached,** fond; **thatch,** straw used in making a roof; **reproach,** blame; **taunt,** mock; **alluded,** referred.

LEARNING BY OBSERVATION

Art, the power of; **natural history,** the study of nature, as of plants and animals; **accustomed,** to become used; **shrewd,** keen or sharp; **tedious,** tiresome; **heath,** used in England to describe a moor or plain overgrown with a low shrub called heather; **peewit,** a kind of gull that flies as if with broken wing to tempt the hunter to follow it and thus saves its nest; **turf,** sod or peat used for fuel in England; **Roman camp,** Romans occupied England from the first to the fifth century; **superiority,** advantage; **acquires,** gets; **Franklin,** Benjamin Franklin; **Channel,** the English Channel, about twenty miles wide between Dover and Calais.

NUREMBERG

Nuremberg is situated on the river Pegnitz in Franconia, a district in Bavaria, Germany. Its picturesque, medieval buildings are probably the best preserved in Europe. **Pegnitz** (peg'-nits); **Franconian** (frang-kō'-ni-an). **Quaint,** old, curious; **traffic,** trade; **gable,** the triangular end of a building; **rooks,** crows; **planted by Queen Cunigunde,** who reigned seven hundred years ago; **mart,** market-place; **sainted Sebald,** the patron saint of

Nuremberg was a hermit who lived in the eighth century; **enshrined,** in a chest; **sainted Laurence,** St. Lorenz; **pix,** a chest in which are kept the bread and wine for the Lord's Supper; **Albrecht Dürer** lived and died in the house which you see to the left in the picture; it has been restored by a Dürer society and is visited yearly by thousands of tourists; **evangelist,** missionary; **emigravit,** Latin for departed; **obscure,** dark; **Mastersingers,** the mechanics of Nuremberg and several other German cities who, in the fifteenth and sixteenth centuries, formed a guild or company for mutual improvement and held contests in poetry and song at regular intervals; **Hans Sachs** (zäks), a picture of whose statue is given, was a shoemaker, born in 1494. He was made immortal by Wagner in his opera, *Die Meistersinger;* **laureate,** crowned with laurel as a victor; **Twelve Wise Masters,** the first of the Mastersingers.

THE WINNING OF THE SWORD

Nourishing, care and support; **a passing true man,** more than ordinarily honest; **a lord of fair livelihood,** having lands and money; **malady,** illness; **realm,** kingdom; **knight,** a soldier of rank in the middle ages who took oath to protect the poor, uphold the right and live a stainless life; **ordained,** ordered; **joust,** (jŭst), a mock duel between two knights on horseback; **tournament,** a sham battle in which a number of knights took part; **commons,** the common people; **foster brother,** brought up or fostered as a brother, but not having the same parents; **beholden unto,** indebted to; **coronation,** the crowning; **bereaved,** deprived; **rendered again,** given back; **prowess,** bravery.

INCIDENT OF THE FRENCH CAMP

Ratisbon, situated on the Danube in Bavaria, Germany, was besieged in 1809 for five days by Napoleon; **prone,** bent forward; **oppressive,** burdened; **mused,** thought over; **ere,** before; **flagbird,** the figure of a bird on Napoleon's flags; **vans,** wings; **sheathes,** covers; **film,** thin skin.

JOAN OF ARC

Domremy (dôṅ-rä-me'); **Meuse** (mūz); **godmother,** a woman who promises at a child's birth to watch over it; **neighboring,** nearby; **industrious,** hard-working; **Dauphin,** the title of the eldest son of the king of France; **vague,** hazy; **prophecy,** a saying about the future; **garrison,** a fort; **succor,** help; **Reims** (rēmz); **to be anointed,** to have oil poured on the head as a sacred ceremony; **herrings,** a kind of fish salted and smoked before eaten; **surcoat,** a long outer coat; **Chinon,** (shē-nôṅ'); **sire,** father, a term of respect often used toward kings; **dawdling,** wasting time; **goad,** force, as a herder would force his cattle with a stick; **Black Prince,** son of Edward III, king of England, so named from the color of his armor. He was famous for his bravery; **Limousin,** (le-mö-zan'); **Tours,** (tör); **foss,** a ditch; **battlements,** the walls of a fort; **Dunois** (dü-nwä'); **onslaught,** attack; **brink,** edge; **miracle,** a supernatural event; **Loire** (lwär), the largest river in France; **brunt,** weight, hardship; **thwarted,** prevented; **avail,** use; **treachery,** falseness; **secretary,** one who attends to the letters and messages of another.

THE PIED PIPER OF HAMELIN

Sprats, herring; **ermine,** a white fur dotted with black, used by royalty; **obese,** fleshy; **civic,** state; **consternation,** horror; **guilder,** about forty cents; **pied,** many-colored; **vesture,** clothing; **Cham** (Käm), King of Tartary, a province of China; **Nizan** (Nezän'), sovereign of a province in India; **adept,** one skilled; **commentaries,** Cæsar's history of his wars in Spain and Italy; **tripe,** the stomach of a cow; **drysaltery,** where salted meats are kept; **puncheon,** a large cask; **staved,** broken in; **perked,** came up saucily; **havoc,** waste; **replenish,** refill; **butt,** cask; **poke,** a pocket; **bate,** give in; **stiver,** about two cents; **ribald,** (rĭb'-ald), a good-for-nothing fellow; **bereft,** deprived; **fallow,** pale yellow; **burgher's pate,** citizen's head; **decree,** law; **Transylvania,** a province in

Austria; **alien,** foreign; **subterraneous,** underground; **trepanned,** trapped.

JOHNNY DARTER

Apparently, plainly; **habits,** ways of living; **appropriate,** suitable; **Rafinesque** (rä-fē-nesk´), a French-American zoölogist; **potluck,** what he might eat; **deserves,** should have, merits; **especial,** particular; **ardent,** strong; **be native,** belong to; **aquarium,** a vessel filled with water for keeping live fish; **peculiarities** (pē-kūl-yăr´ ĭ-ties), that which makes them different from other fish; **species,** kinds; **vertical,** upright; **alternating,** every other one; **base of the tail,** where the tail joins the body; **ground hue,** general color underneath; **marbled,** streaked like colored marble; **intervals,** now and then; **regain,** get back; **induced,** brought on; **pigment,** color; **blended,** mixed together; **old Izaak,** Izaak Walton, a London shopkeeper who lived in the seventeenth century, and became famous as the author of *The Complete Angler.*

SNOW-BOUND

Firmament, sky; **Chinese roof,** slanting like a pagoda; **Pisa's leaning miracle,** the bell tower of the cathedral in Pisa, Italy, which is 181 feet high and leans almost fourteen feet to the south; **mimic,** imitation; **pendent trammels,** hanging hooks; **somber,** gloomy; **baffled,** checked; **silhouette,** a shadow picture.

DAN AND UNA

Rehearsed, practised; **pointy-eared,** having pointed ears; "**They were not, of course, allowed to act on Midsummer Night**", midsummer day, June 23, is kept as a festival in honor of the birth of John the Baptist; "**apricocks**", apricots; **unthistly,** without thistles; **hempen home-spuns,** homely fellows; **swaggering,** in a boasting manner; **toward,** near at hand; **auditor,** one who hears; **Scholars,** wise men; **Merlin,** an enchanter famous in early English legends.

TITANIA AND OBERON

Thorough, an old form of "through," now obsolete except in such words as "thoroughfare" and "thoroughly;" **pale,** paling; **swifter than the moon's sphere,** faster than the moon; **pensioners,** handsome, tall young men attached to the queen's court; **lob,** clown; **anon,** soon; **passing fell,** very angry; **changeling,** a child exchanged for another, by fairies; **perforce,** by force; **sheen,** brightness; **square,** quarrel; **shrewd,** quick, sharp-witted; **knavish,** mischievous; **sprite,** a fairy; **villagery,** several villages; **quern,** a hand mill for grinding grain; **bootless,** useless; **barm,** foam; **filly foal,** a colt; **lurk,** lie hidden; **a gossip's bowl,** the drink of an old woman; **crab,** a crab-apple; **dewlap,** skin hanging under the chin; **"tailor" cries,** an expression of anger and contempt; **waxen in their mirth,** laughing more heartily; **Ere the leviathan can swim a league,** the leviathan, a whale, is able to swim a great distance in a short time. A league is about three miles; **exit,** Latin for going out; plural, exeunt, used when more than one person leaves; **thyme** (tīm), a garden plant with a spicy taste; **oxlips,** cowslips; **over-canopied,** overhung; **luscious,** delicious, melting; **eglantine,** a kind of rose; **lull'd,** soothed; **enamel'd,** overlaid; **fantasies,** fancies; **roundel,** a dance in a circle; **cankers,** worms; **reremice,** bats; **clamorous,** wailing; **quaint spirits,** dainty frolics; **offices,** duties; **hedgehog,** a kind of hog whose hair is prickly; **newt,** a lizard; **Philomel,** the nightingale; **languish,** grieve; **ounce,** an animal resembling the leopard; **Pard,** leopard; **Pyramus** (pir'-a-mus), and **Thisbe** (Thiz'-bē), famous lovers in an old legend; **translated,** changed; **set his wit to,** answer; **enamor'd,** pleased with; **enthralled,** bound; **gleek,** jest; **grossness,** heaviness; **courteous,** polite; **gambol in his eyes,** play before him; **crop,** to gather a crop; **to fan the moonbeams,** moonlight was supposed to be injurious; **Mounsieur,** Bottom wishes to use "Monsieur", French for "Mister", but does not quite know how to say it; **humble-bee,** bumblebee; **signior** (sē'-nyor), an Italian title like our "sir" or "Mister"; **neaf,** hand; **Cavalery,** Bottom means cavalier, a gallant gentleman.

A LIST OF BOOKS FOR HOME READING

Edited for Child Classics by Hamilton Wright Mabie

My library
Was dukedom large enough.
　　　　—William Shakespeare.

†MABIE, HAMILTON WRIGHT
    (EDITOR) . . . . *Norse Stories*

†MABIE, HAMILTON WRIGHT
    (EDITOR) . . . . *Heroes Every Child Should Know*

MACDONALD, GEORGE . . . . *At the Back of the North Wind*

MOFFETT, CLEVELAND . . . . *Careers of Danger and Daring*

MOORES, CHARLES W. . . . *Life of Abraham Lincoln for Boys and Girls*

NORTON, CHARLES ELIOT
    (EDITOR) . . . . *Heart of Oak Books, III, IV and V*

PAGE, THOMAS NELSON . . . *Two Little Confederates*

PYLE, HOWARD . . . . . *Pepper and Salt*

RASPE, R. E. (EDITED BY E. E. HALE) . . . . . . *Tales from Münchhausen*

RUSKIN, JOHN . . . . . *The King of the Golden River*

SEAWELL, MOLLY ELLIOT . . . *Little Jarvis*

SETON-THOMPSON, ERNEST . *Wild Animals I Have Known*

SETON-THOMPSON, ERNEST . *The Biography of a Grizzly*

STOCKTON, FRANK R. . . . *Fanciful Tales*

SWIFT, JONATHAN . . . . *Gulliver's Travels*

WARNER, CHARLES DUDLEY . *A-Hunting of the Deer*

*WHITTIER, JOHN GREENLEAF . *Complete Poetical Works*

WIGGIN, KATE DOUGLAS . . *Timothy's Quest*

WIGGIN AND SMITH (EDITORS) . *The Fairy Ring*

WIGGIN AND SMITH (EDITORS) . *A Book of Laughter Tales*

*Poetry.
†Added by the Editors of *Child Classics.*

SUGGESTIONS TO TEACHERS

1. Know your lesson—both its literary possibilities and its technical difficulties.

2. Know your class—both as children whose lives are to be affected for good by the inspiration they are to receive through this lesson with you, and as readers with varying powers to interpret the printed page.

The reading lesson should be a social exercise. Children of this age have acquired considerable power of independent study, and they should come to the recitation prepared to contribute individually and abundantly to the pleasure of the whole class. Such a result is possible when the teacher throws upon the class all the responsibility it can carry.

Children are able and are delighted to do far more than the average teacher realizes or permits. Let them ask some of the questions and make some of the criticisms. Insist upon large, suggestive, helpful criticism. Do not permit such superficial comment as: " Miss ——, Johnny said *in* for *it*." Rather, require one child to address the other kindly, " I get a different thought. It seems to me it should be read in this way." You are working for power, not information. Do not become discouraged if their questions are not so good as yours, the first week or the second; and above all do not think you are wasting time. Train the children to ask keen questions, to pass by the nine unimportant questions and to ask the tenth pertinent one. In less time than you realize the pupils will be demanding of each other clarity of thought and finished style beyond anything you could get. The cause is the child's self-activity.

It would seem therefore that the teacher should become a trainer of teachers of reading. To do this she must be able to read herself, to sense the lesson in all its literary values, and to get a corresponding response from her class. Five books especially helpful in such work are Hinsdale's

Teaching of the Language Arts and *Art of Study*, Chubb's *The Teaching of English*; Baker, Carpenter and Scott's *The Teaching of English* and Carson's *The Voice and Spiritual Education.*

Reading lessons fall into two types, extensive and intensive—sight reading and study reading. The division is based upon the difficulty of the text, not on any inherent difference in the nature of the selection. A lesson that would be intensive reading for *The Third Reader* pupil, would, in all probability, be extensive reading for *The Fourth Reader* pupil. The child should have both kinds of work, for through one he acquires facility in expression, and through the other power to get deeper thought.

Little need be said on extensive reading. It should be pure pleasure. The teacher may seat herself among the children, who with books closed listen to several who read in turn such stories as *Turning the Grindstone*, or who dramatize impromptu *The Gray Swan*.

Intensive reading is the test of the teacher. There is no limit to the artistic skill she may put forth. A few general principles may be in place.

The selection should be presented as a whole to the class before they begin to analyze it. This can be done in a poem by the teacher's reading through the entire piece to key the class through her voice to its spiritual pitch; or in a narrative, by assigning it as a story to be read during study time and reproduced orally in outline. Following this study of the whole will come, first, the study of the larger literary units, such as, in *Tom, the Chimney Sweep*, Tom, the journey, the arrival, etc.; and after that the careful study of the single sentence.

Great opportunity for developing the child's taste is afforded in the home reading lists. There is no substitute in this matter for personal interest on the part of the teacher. One good way to interest children in a book is to read to them a part of the story. The book can then be lent over night to some child who will tell to the class the next day what he has read. The teacher may continue for a few moments the reading of the story that the class shall again feel the author's power and style and the book then be given to another child for further report.

The child's constructive imagination should constantly be appealed to. Ask him, for instance, to give in his own words the picture described in the first four stanzas of *The Inchcape Rock;* to dramatize *Christmas at the Cratchits'*, embellishing the dialogue with appropriate action and adding dialogue if it can be done effectively.

Children delight to make original drawings and could be asked to illustrate such selections as *The Reverie of Poor Susan*, *The House in Bidwell Street*, and *How They Brought the Good News from Ghent to Aix*.

Clear-cut enunciation, erect carriage, the light falling properly on the book, are matters which should need no comment.

Edwin Ramer,
Nappanee,
Ind,

R, R, # 1